"PLEASE BE ADVISED THAT THE BOOK, AND THE AUTHORS OF THE BOOK, ARE NOT AFFILIATED, IN ANY WAY, WITH INSTRUMENTS OR SOUND HEALING TECHNIQUES USED AND TAUGHT UNDER THE SERVICE MARK ACUTONICS TM."

Acutone

A New System of Healing Based on the Ancient Science of Sound

By
Dean Lloyd
and
John Pirog

La Mesa Holistic Health Center
La Mesa, California

Book Design and Layout: Richard Bradshaw
Cover Design: Cliff Billmeyer
Illustrator: Cliff Billmeyer
Desktop Publisher: Richard Bradshaw
Photographer: Robin Landholm

First Edition
Published in 2000 by
The La Mesa Holistic Health Center
8356 Allison Avenue
La Mesa, California 91941

Printed in Canada

ISBN: 0-9676985-0-2

To Dean's loving wife Debi.

Table of Contents

Acknowledgements

The authors are greatly indebted to the work of Professors Chen Cheng-Yih and Lothar Von Falkenhausen, two of the world's leading authorities in the field of Chinese musical archaeology. We are grateful for the pioneering research of Fabien Maman, the first acupuncturist to use tuning forks as a means of stimulating points, and the first to associate the twelve notes of the chromatic scale with the twelve meridians. Dean is indebted to Lou Paxton Price, who helped him reconstruct Chinese pipes, and whose writings called his attention to the octavic relationship between color and tone. Dean is also grateful to Am Rosen, N.D., for providing him with the motivation to turn his insights into a book. Finally, John thanks Renee for all the help she has given him with his math.

Preface

My earliest memories as a child were of the sounds of birds singing in the trees behind my parent's house in rural Michigan. Each morning when I woke up, I lay in my bed with my eyes still closed, drinking in the voices of life that came from just outside my window. *How beautiful that music could be.* As I grew older, I began to look for this same sense of beauty in all the sounds around our small home—the sighing of wind, the rustle of trees, the tingling of the bells on my sled. No matter where I went, I was greeted by the endless tones of nature.

Eventually, my fascination with the world of sound led me to explore the world of music. It seemed that each instrument spoke to me with its own unique voice, and each song carried me to its own unique place. I came to believe that I could create any mood, any thought, any feeling—even the feeling of love—if I could just find the right melody, the right blend of tones. As long as I had music, I was in complete control of my life!

And then one day I had a terrible accident. I was knocked down while skating on an ice rink, my head hitting the ice with a crack. When I awoke in the emergency room, the world around me was buzzing with strange noises. I watched as if through a cloud as my father spoke worriedly with the doctor. The pain in my head was unbearable. But when I closed my eyes, I began to hear a faint tone coming from somewhere deep inside me. As I focused my mind on that tone, the pain began to subside.

I continued to suffer from headaches for many years after that accident. But each time I felt the pain returning, I listened for the healing tone, resonating it through my mind until the headache went away. Sometimes I would try to hum it; other times I would rush home from school to try to reproduce it on a guitar or a double bass. Although the pitch was always different, it never failed to relieve my pain. I eventually came to realize that my musical path had intersected with the path of healing. *If I can resonate with a healing tone, I can be healed!*

I carried this thought with me as I entered Acupuncture school. The ancient Chinese, I soon learned, were the world's great masters of the science of sound. Long ago they had discovered a system for healing with tone, but their techniques and even their music had become lost in history. My co-author and I have spent the last five years trying to recover this lost system, and the result of our research is the method we have named "Acutone."

At some point in our lives, each and every one of us has been touched by the healing power of sound. We have used music to raise broken spirits and heal broken hearts. We have whispered songs to soften discord and calm the tears of infants. Perhaps we have listened quietly, as I did in my youth, for the healing voice of nature. Our goal in writing this book is to provide you with a method for finding the unique harmony that you naturally seek in life, and for communicating that harmony to those who cry out for your help.

If you can resonate the healing tone, you can heal!

Dean Lloyd
February 2000

Introduction

We would like to introduce the reader to a new and unique form of Oriental healing, one that uses pure sound to harmonize the meridians and to invigorate the body's energy. We call our technique *Acutone*. It is a powerful and effective technique, and we believe you will find it as valuable to your practice as it has been to ours. This book will teach you all you need to know to get started with this therapy, assuming you have a basic background in acupuncture or Oriental bodywork.

Acutone is a complete system of natural healing; it can be used alone or in concert with other Oriental therapies such as acupuncture, moxabustion, or Oriental bodywork. Its methodology is based on scrupulous research of the Chinese classics and extensive experience by the authors and their predecessors. The primary instruments used in Acutone are tuning forks, and all the techniques are non-invasive. We chose tuning forks because they produce the purest tone of any natural instrument, and because they can be easily applied to the body, much like the non-penetrating *Teishins* of modern Japan.

But Acutone tone acupuncture is much more than another type of acupressure/acupuncture. The tuning fork transmits a pure tone that travels deeper through the body's tissues and much faster than the vibration of an acupuncture needle. Furthermore, the Acutone system is founded on the ancient principle that there are definite frequencies that affect each of the five-phases as well as the twelve meridians.

Our story of Acutone began in Wisconsin with Dean Lloyd, an acupuncturist and musician. Having completed a course of study in five-phase acupuncture, Dean learned of an obscure treatise in the *Huang Di Nei Jing*, the Yellow Emperor's Inner Classic. It explained how the five notes of the Chinese pentatonic scale ruled over the energies of the five yin meridians (see chapter 1). Although the *Nei Jing* was clearly inviting its readers to employ the five tones as a form of therapy, it did not provide clear details on how the tones should be used. Also, it is likely that the ancient Chinese would have used bells and flutes in therapy, since tuning forks were not invented until the 18th century in Europe.

Using the pitch standards derived from a modern Oriental reference, Dean fashioned an experiment that assessed pulse changes in human subjects while tones were played with a flute. A Doppler meter was used to ensure objectivity of the pulse measurements. While the playing of the tones had a discernible impact on the pulse readings, the changes produced were opposite those required for healing, i.e., excess pulses became more excess and so on. We now realize that the main reason for the failure was the employment of modern pitch standards that were not the same as those used in the true Chinese scale of ancient times.

When Dean heard of a visiting French researcher who had developed a method of healing with tuning forks, he traveled to the West Coast to confer with him. There he met Fabien Maman, a musician/composer turned acupuncturist who had spent twenty years researching the effects of resonance on the body. Fabien's discovery of the power of tone began when he was leading a concert in Tokyo in 1974. Unlike Western audiences, it was not the custom of the Japanese to applaud at the conclusion of each piece.

> *The silence after each piece was bewildering at first... But after the initial apprehension at the end of the first few pieces, I began to anticipate and even enjoy the silence. I could sense that the silence was filled with the resonance of the music just played and so I took the opportunity after each piece to feel the real effect the music was having on myself, the other performers, the audience and even the concert hall itself. I could tell that the music affected the body and spirit of the audience and musicians alike—and that the particular effect differed with each piece played.*

Fabien eventually put his performance career on hold in order to learn acupuncture, Aikido, and Kototama, the science of pure sound. After years of experimentation, Fabien was able to develop a system of correspondence between the sixty antique-*shu* points and the twelve notes of the modern chromatic scale. It is to Fabien's research with antique points that much of the present book is indebted. Dean's own experience, however, has added significant new dimensions to the application of tone in Chinese healing, including the use of the pentatonic scale in five-phase treatment and the invention of the Resonance Bell.

The final Acutone system as presented here is highly flexible and makes available the full spectrum of techniques used by the modern acupuncturist and body therapist. We must point out, however, that although Acutone is based on music theory, it is a form of *tone therapy*, not music therapy. The tuning forks are used to resonate through the cellular medium in the body's tissues, not through the auditory canal. The technique can be used even if the patient is deaf. Also, while tuning forks have become popular with "New Age" healers, Acutone is the first attempt to make systematic use of the true Chinese pentatonic scale based on the ancient *Huang Zhong* fundamental. As the reader will soon learn, this is the scale upon which the five-phases and the twelve meridians were originally patterned.

It is impossible to underestimate the importance that scales and music played in the genesis of Chinese civilization. Music was seen as the concrete manifestation of the natural order and harmony that permeated the universe. The playing of music was a way of ritually embracing this cosmic harmony, and thus music and ritual (*li*) were inextricably linked.

> *Music appeared in the Great Beginning, and the rituals* (li) *took their place on the completion of things. What manifests itself without ceasing is Heaven, what manifests itself without stirring is Earth. Movement and quiescence sum up all between Heaven and Earth. And so the Sages would simply speak about rituals and music.*[1]

> *A Minister of Ritual* (Da Zong Bo) *was one who used music to "adjust the transformations of Heaven and Earth and the production of all material things."*[2] *Music, in short, was a way of regulating, through human intervention, the creative forces at work in the world. In this manner, music and musical tones have a direct impact on the process of healing.*

Although our goal in writing this book is to present our profession with a practical healing methodology, there is much in the following pages that will be of interest to modern scholars as well. The evidence will show that the five-phases, long thought to be an invention of the late Zhou Dynasty, were based on musical precursors that are as old as Chinese civilization itself. Furthermore, this musical paradigm continued to underlie the

---

[1] *Li Ji* ch. 28, as quoted in Fung Yu-Lan 1931, p. 344.
[2] *Zhou Li* , as quoted in Von Falkenhausen p. 2.

framework of cosmological theory and was incorporated into the very matrix of the meridian circulation scheme designed by the authors of the *Nei Jing*.

The Acutone therapy presented in this book is composed of two interlocking acupuncture sub-systems: the five-phases and the twelve meridians. We will demonstrate how these two sub-systems interface closely with the two great scales of Chinese history, the pentatonic and the chromatic respectively. This does not exhaust all the Acutone applications, however, and future works will explore the eight extraordinary vessels, auricular therapy, and the Indian chakra systems.

The tools required for Acutone are relatively simple and inexpensive, and include a full chromatic scale of tuning forks. Resources for purchasing tuning forks as well as the Acutone Resonance Bell can be found in Appendix D. We also invite the reader to explore the work of Fabien Maman, *Sound and Acupuncture: The Body as Harp*.

We wish the reader success in this great healing adventure, and look forward to meeting you in our workshops.

Dean Lloyd
John Pirog
1999

Chapter I

Creation of the Chinese Pentatonic Scale

1. The Science of Scales

Throughout the history of the world, wherever and whenever music has been played, the various pitches have been arranged to form a *scale*. The creation of a scale is made necessary by the nature of sound itself. Out of the infinite frequencies available, a fixed and finite series of tones must be chosen upon which songs and melodies can be reproduced. A musical scale is organized from the lower pitches to the higher, allowing the voice or musical instrument to "ascend" in an orderly manner through a hierarchy of precisely measured steps. To the ancient Chinese, this naturally occurring hierarchy was the patent model upon which social order should be formed and against which human evolution should be measured.

Inherent to the creation of any scale is the human perception, gleaned by intuition and confirmed by mathematical insight,

1

that any two tones sounded together will be harmonious or dissonant. Further, that the most harmonious relationship for any given tone is with that tone which is double (or half) its own frequency. In a modern Just scale, the note C_4 has a frequency of 264 Hz. If we double this we have 528 Hz, which is the frequency of C_5. The relationship thus established, 264/528, a ratio of 1:2, is called the *octave*.

Virtually all musical scales in history have been founded upon the octave. This means that the various notes available to the musician are placed between the lowest note of a scale, called the *key-note*, and its higher octave. The notes above the key-note are arranged in precisely measured steps. The difference in frequency between any two notes in the scale is referred to as an *interval*. In our modern C-major scale, the octave is divided into seven steps or intervals represented by the white keys on the pianoforte. The ordinal number of a note on this scale is also the name given to the interval which that note forms with the key-note:

C_5	octave
B_4	seventh
A_4	sixth
G_4	fifth
F_4	fourth
E_4	third
D_4	second
C_4	key-note

After the octave, the simplest ratio between frequencies is 2:3. This is the second most harmonious interval between notes, referred to as a *perfect fifth* in Western musical nomenclature. In the C-major scale above, the ratio of C_4 to G_4 is 2:3 (264/396) and therefore G is said to be the perfect fifth of C.

The character of a scale is determined, in part, by the distribution of notes and sequence of intervals within the octave. Ancient Greek musicians discovered long ago that new interval patterns or *modes* could be created by shifting the starting point of the octave to a different note contained in the same scale. Each Greek mode had its own unique character, and this allowed musicians playing simple stringed instruments to enjoy a rich musical variety with the same recipe of tones. The C-major scale—referred to as the *Lydian* mode—has shorter intervals (half-steps) between E – F, i.e., between the third and fourth steps; and between B – C, i.e., between the seventh and eighth steps (Figure1.1). If we shift the order of tones in this scale so that it starts at B, (the so-called *Mixolydian* mode), the shorter intervals will still occur between B – C and E – F, but their sequential placement will change so that they now occur between the first and second steps and between the fourth and fifth steps accordingly. So long as the intervalic structure of a given mode is maintained, any tone can be used as a starting point.

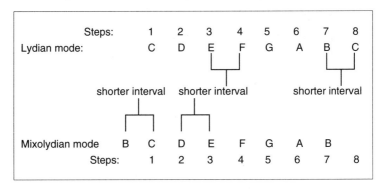

Figure 1.1 Lydian, Mixolydian Mode

Modes are critical to the understanding of Chinese music and the function of the Chinese scale. In modern Western music, however, mode-change has been rare, and variety is instead produced by transposing music to different *keys*. When the key of a scale changes, its key-note changes without any shift in the sequential positions of the intervals. This requires that the notes themselves change, and this usually requires an interface with a chromatic scale that can provide the necessary half-steps. Although key transposition is beyond the scope of the present work, it played a critical role in the development ancient Chinese musicology.

All scales must be derived from a single pitch or frequency, called a *fundamental*. This frequency is used to generate a series of harmonic ratios, and from these ratios are derived the scale's intervals and—by extension—its notes. In single-mode Western music, the fundamental is the lowest note of the scale. In the major scale just described, for example, the fundamental is C. We have already seen how the ratios 1:2 and 2:3 define the intervals of the octave and the perfect fifth respectively. If we continue to build ratios through a *harmonic series*, we can create all the intervals necessary for the generation of a scale (Figure 1.2).

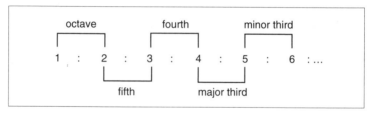

Figure 1.2 Harmonic Series

Because there are seven notes in the octave, the Western major scale belongs to a species of scale called *heptatonic*. Although heptatonic scales have been found on ancient Chinese bone-flutes as early as the sixth millennium B.C.,[3] the Chinese civilization has shown a decisive preference for a simpler scale, called *pentatonic*, with *five* notes to the octave. Let us examine how the Chinese pentatonic scale came into being.

2. Ling Lun and His Pipes

In ancient China, birds were seen as messengers of heaven, and sages listened for omens in their songs[4]. The oldest musical instruments were bone and bamboo pipes made to mimic these

---

3 Chen Cheng Yih, Xi Ze-Zong, Jao Tsung-I, 1994, p. 306-307.
4 Walters, p. 17.

sounds[5], and a series of such pipes formed the earliest Chinese musical scale. It was perhaps believed that a scale so produced would confer upon those who used it some portion of the bird's ability to ascend to the heavens.

According to legend, the Yellow Emperor assigned to his master musician, Ling Lun, the task of establishing the pitches of the scale. To accomplish this, Ling Lun had to journey to a remote valley north of Kun Lun Mountain in search of a unique bamboo reed that grew naturally uniform in thickness and aperture. Finding this, he proceeded to cut different lengths of reed into a series of pitch-pipes (*lu guan*), and these became the notes of the first chromatic scale.[6] Ancient pitch-pipes were indeed made from lengths of bamboo, cut between the joints and closed on one end. By blowing gently into the open hole, in a manner similar to blowing into an empty bottle, ancient musicians found they could produce a clear tone with a measured frequency inversely related to the length of the pipe. Assuming the pipes all had identical apertures, the longer the pipe, the lower was the tone and vice versa.

Such use of the breath to create a sustained frequency has profound mystical and medical significance. Human respiration is the quintessential manifestation of *qi*, the energy of life. The movement of qi through a pitch-pipe is analogous to the movement of qi through an acupuncture meridian, and just as each length of pitch-pipe will create its own unique frequency of tone, so will each meridian create its own unique "frequency" of qi.

Returning to the above story, Ling Lun was said to have established his scale upon a fundamental pitch-pipe that was 3 *cun* 9 *fen* (3.9 *cun*) long. As far back as the fifth century B.C., this fundamental pitch-pipe has been called the *Huang Zhong*, literally, the "Yellow Bell." Since yellow is the color of the Earth phase (see Table 1.1), it is likely that the *Huang Zhong* pitch

---

[5] Von Falkenhausen, p. 123.

[6] The legend is recorded in the *Lu Shi Chun Qiu* (*Springs and Autumns of Master Lu*, c. 235 B.C.). See Chen Cheng Yih, 1996, pp. 6 for a full translation of this story.

was conceived to be the fundamental frequency of the earth itself; of the foundation and center point of the universe.[7]

Wood	Fire		Earth	Metal	Water
A#	C#		F#	G#	D#
Jue	Zhi		Gong	Shang	Yu
Liver	Heart	Pericardium	Spleen	Lung	Kidney
Gall Bladder	Small Intestine	Tripple Warmer	Stomach	Large Intestine	Unrinary Bladder
East	South		Center	West	North
Spring	Summer		Late Summer	Fall	Winter
Wind	Heat		Damp	Dry	Cold
Sinews	Capillaries		Flesh	Skin	Bones
Shouting	Laughing		Singing	Weeping	Moaning
Jupiter	Mars		Saturn	Venus	Mercury
Blue-Green	Red		Yellow	White	Blue-Black
Sour	Bitter		Sweet	Acrid	Salty
Pipes	Strings		Okarina	Bells	Drums
8	7		5	9	6

Table 1.1 Five Phase Correspondences

Through measurements taken of various surviving instruments from the Han Dynasty and earlier, we estimate that the frequency of the *Huang Zhong* pitch-pipe approximates F# in our modern Western scale.[8]

In the *Shi Ji* (Record of the Historian, c. 2nd century B.C.), the length of the *Huang Zhong* pitch pipe is given as 8 *cun* 1 *fen*.[9] Since 10 *fen* equals 1 *cun*, this adjusts the length of the *Huang*

---

[7] Chen Cheng-Yih, 1996, p. 70.

[8] Estimates of the Han Dynasty *Huang Zhong* range from F# to G#. The reason for the present authors' preference for F# will become evident in chapter 5 and Appendix I.

[9] As translated in Van Falkenhausen, p. 300.

Zhong pitch-pipe to 81 *fen*, slightly more than double the length recorded in the earlier story. The two *Huang Zhong's* may have simply been higher and lower octaves of the same or similar tone. To the Chinese, however, the *Huang Zhong* pipe and the musical scale it generated was the spiritual basis for the whole of civilization; we must therefore assume that the length of the pipe was a musical way of expressing some primordial numerological truth.

To begin with, the number 81 serves a practical purpose: it is the smallest number that can be evenly divided four times by the number 3. As we are about to see, this allows it to generate the series of notes that form the Chinese pentatonic scale. More importantly, 81 is the square of 9, or the 4th power of 3. The familiar Chinese magic square is divided nine-fold (Figure 1.3). To the ancients, the squares of whole numbers were considered magical because they were the geometric expression of the creation process. When a line is squared, a plane is created, and thus *dimensional existence* has been brought into being.

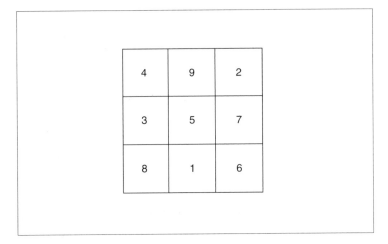

Figure 1.3 Chinese Magic Square

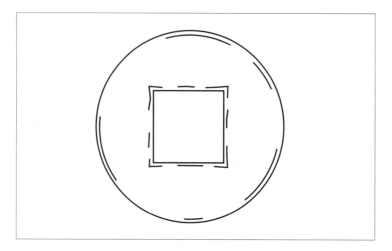

Figure 1.4 Ancient Chinese Coin

The quintessential symbol of dimensional space was the Earth itself, which was represented in Figure form by a square surrounded by the circle of Heaven, as seen in the shape of the ancient Chinese coin (Figure1.4). The Yellow Emperor was looking for the fundamental frequency of the earth "plane," a musical tone that contained the secret of spatial existence and the geometric beginning of form. The earlier *Huang Zhong* length of 3 *cun* plus 9 *fen* was likely a similar attempt to create a pitch measurement that was built exponentially from a base of 3, since 3 *cun* 9 *fen* is equivalent to 3.9 *cun* or 39 *fen*, and the cube root of 39 is approximately 3.39.

The numerological basis of the scale is expressed most explicitly in the *Guan Zhi* (*Book of Master Guan*, c. 4th century B.C.), which generates the five pentatonic notes from abstract numerical values. The relevant passage begins as follows:

> *Concerning the creation of the five notes,*
> *begin by taking the* Primordial One [zhu yi],
> *then multiply it by 3. The fourth power of this*
> *number gives 9 X 9 (i.e., 81), and this is the*
> *smallest leading number in the generation*

8

> [sheng] [of the scale] *from* [the note called]
> Gong *in the* Huang Zhong *pitch*.[10]

Once again a value of 81 is given to the *Huang Zhong* pitch, and the preface clearly establishes the importance of deriving this number exponentially from 3, which is in turn derived from the "Primordial One." Having established the importance of the *Huang Zhong* pitch, let us now examine how it was used to generate the notes of the pentatonic scale. In order to make the *Guan Zi* formula more concrete, let us imagine that the given values of the notes refer to lengths, measured in *fen*, of equal-diameter pitch-pipes.[11]

As the passage above states, the fundamental note of the pentatonic scale is called **Gong**, its frequency being identical to that of the *Huang Zhong*, since it comes from a pitch-pipe that is 81 *fen* long. It corresponds with the note F# in a modern scale (Figure 1.5).

---

[10] For the full text of the passage see Chen Cheng-Yih, 1994, p. 151.

[11] The numerical values quoted here from the *Guan Zi* follow an ancient formula that was largely theoretical. In an actual pitch-pipe, frequency is a function of diameter as well as length. In a set of equal-aperture pipes, therefore, minute adjustments would have to be made in the lengths of the four succeeding pipes in order to make up for the lack of change in diameter. The classics do not provide any written guidance for these alterations, and it is possible that the musicians made the adjustments by ear.

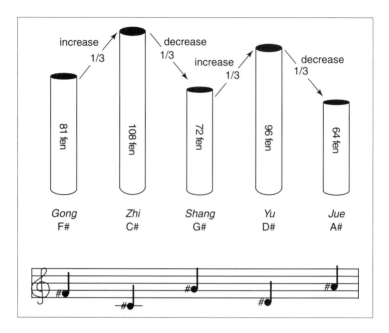

Figure 1.5 Five Pitch Pipes With Notes

If we continue to follow the generation formula recorded in the *Guan Zi*, the second note in the scale is created by increasing the length of the *Gong* pitch-pipe by 1/3; this produces a pipe that is 4/3 the length of *Gong*, or 108 *fen*. The note thus generated is called **Zhi**, which corresponds with C# in a modern scale. Since pitch frequency is in inverse proportion to length of pitch-pipe, the note *Zhi* (C#) is a fourth *below Gong* (F#).

The next note in the series was generated by cutting the length of the *Zhi* pipe by 1/3. This produces a pipe 2/3 the size *Zhi*, or 72 *fen*. The note thus generated is called **Shang**–G# in modern nomenclature. *Shang* (G#) is a perfect fifth *above Zhi* (C#).

The *Shang* pipe was then increased by 1/3 to 96 *fen*, generating the note **Yu** or D#, a fourth below *Shang*. Finally, the *Yu* pipe was cut by 1/3 to 64 *fen* to generate **Jue** or A#, a fifth above *Yu*.

The above process is referred to as *san fen sun yi fa*, roughly, "the technique of adding and subtracting one third." Arranging the five frequencies as consecutive notes within an octave, the above technique produces a pentatonic scale in the *Zhi* mode (see Table 1.2).

C#	D#	F#	G#	A#
Zhi	Yu	Gong	Shang	Jue

Table 1.2 Zhi Mode

By reformulating the sequence of additions and subtractions, we can produce five different pentatonic modes (*wu diao*). It is the *Gong* mode which is of greatest interest to us in the present discussion, however, since the scale just described is created by a process called "generation by the fifth," (*wu du xiang sheng*). By taking *Gong* as the fundamental and arranging the notes in ascending fifths, the following pattern emerges:

perfect fifth   perfect fifth   perfect fifth   perfect fifth
Gong(F#) $\longrightarrow$ Zhi(C#) $\longrightarrow$ Shang(G#) $\longrightarrow$ Yu(D#) $\longrightarrow$ Jue(A#)

This lineage of fifths is the heart of the Chinese pentatonic scale. The sequence *must* start on *Gong* since the cycle of fifths ends at *Jue*, there being no ascending perfect fifth from A# in the scale (the interval from A# to F# is an augmented fifth). Because the Yellow Emperor's scale was generated from perfect fifths, the most harmonious of all musical intervals, it was believed to confer health and harmony on all the beings that came in contact with it. The pentatonic scale, with its five perfectly related frequencies, was therefore the natural precursor for what later became known as the five-phases.

3. The Pentatonic Scale and The Five-Phases

In the late Zhou dynasty, each of the five tones in the pentatonic scale came to be formally associated with one of the five-phases.[12] Let us look at the scale in the *Gong* mode (see Table 1.2) together with the phases associated with each note:

F#	G#	A#	C#	D#
Gong	Shang	Jue	Zhi	Yu
Earth	Metal	Wood	Fire	Water

Table 1.3 Gong Mode

Note that the five-phase sequence produced by ascending from Gong in the pentatonic scale is Earth → Metal → Wood → Fire → Water. This is a permutation of the five-phases quite distinct from the two sequences most familiar to practitioners of Chinese healing, the Generation (*Sheng*) cycle (Earth → Metal → Water → Wood → Fire) and Restraint (*Ke*) cycle (Earth → Water → Fire → Metal→ Wood) (see Figure 3.1).

Taken together, the generation and restraint cycles were meant to represent the process of *endurance*, of life sustained in a harmonious balance between growth and dissolution, like the balance between births and deaths in a stable population. The idea is not dissimilar to the modern medical concept of homeostasis. We might imagine, for example, that too much "growth" in the human body might produce tumors or obesity, while too much "dissolution" might cause anemia and wasting. But if growth and dissolution, i.e., generation and restraint, are kept in a state of balance, the total organism can be sustained indefinitely in a state of health. This is often seen as the goal of Chinese medical practice.

But the five-phase sequence founded on the pentatonic scale has a different function: it embodies the process of *evolution-*

---

[12] The association between the Five-phases and the five tones was first made in the *Yue Ling* (*Monthly Commands*, 3rd century B.C.) and later in the *Huai Nan Zi* (*Lord of Huai Nan*, 2nd century B.C.) (See Fung Yu-Lan 1934, p. 13). The association is further reiterated in Ch. 64-65 of the *Ling Shu* (*Mystical Pivot*, Liansheng Wu, Nelson and Andrew Qi Wu, transl.).

ary change, not of mere static balance. The evolution from lower to higher tones symbolizes the growth from infancy to maturity, from lower to higher consciousness. This evolutionary growth was the principle task that ancient Chinese society set out for itself, and its accomplishment was the anointed function of its rulers. With the advent of the Han Dynasty, however, the emphasis of Chinese civilization underwent a shift that took the five-phase theory out of its original evolutionary context. As the Han rulers struggled to keep their newly formed empire together, the need to sustain an integrative balance in society was deemed to be more immediately important than the evolution of human consciousness.

But echoes of the earlier musical paradigm continued to survive in five-phase cosmology and medical practice. Let us look, for example at the earliest known reference to the five-phases, in the *Hung Fan* (*Grand Norm*) section of the *Shu Jing* (*Classic of History*, c. 4th century B.C.):

> *Of the five-phases, the first is Water; the second Fire; the third Wood; the fourth Metal; the fifth Earth.*[13]

This enumeration order is referred to by Joseph Needham as the *Cosmogonic Sequence* of the five-phases,[14] a term which we shall now adopt. If we connect the five-phases in this sequence with the respective notes in the pentatonic scale, we have:

Water	→	Fire	→	Wood	→	Metal	→	Earth
D#		C#		A#		G#		F#

This is nothing other than a movement *down* the pentatonic scale, i.e., from the highest note to the lowest, in the *Gong* mode. Remember that water was seen as the symbol of the Tao,

---

[13] This passage transl. Fung Yu-Lan, 1934, p. 14.
[14] Needham, Joseph, 1956, pp. 243, 254-255.

the fluid formlessness out of which the myriad forms of this world came into being. The message of the Cosmogonic Sequence was that creation descends from the highest frequency—that of Water, to the lowest—that of Earth, like rain precipitating downward from heaven.[15]

But there is an even deeper meaning hidden in the *Shu Jing* passage cited above. In effect, the text has assigned a *number* to each phase, i.e., 1 to Water; 2 to Fire; 3 to Wood; and so on. If we continue to count upwards in the Cosmogonic Sequence, we will find that the number assignments coincide with the traditional numerological associations attached to the five-phases (see Table 1.1). We now have an explanation for something that has bewildered generations of acupuncturists. When arranged in sequence, these numbers are designed to spell out the pentatonic scale (see Table 1.4):[16]

1	2	3	4	5
Water	Fire	Wood	Metal	Earth
D#	C#	A#	G#	F#

6	7	8	9	(10)
Water	Fire	Wood	Metal	(Earth)
D#	C#	A#	G#	(F#)

Table 1.4 Pentatonic Scale

---

[15] The connection between the "Cosmogonic Sequence" and the pentatonic scale seems to have escaped most authors, including Needham himself (See Needham, 1956, p. 255). By combining the Cosmogonic Sequence from the *Shu Jing* with Appendix II of the *I Ching*, Fung Yu-Lan was able to explain the number associations, although he did not see the further connection that could be made with the pentatonic scale (see Fung Yu-Lan, 1934, p. 14).

[16] The sequence is designed to create an iconic number nine, and so the number 10, which would logically be associated with Earth, is left out. At first glance, this would seem to require a shift to the *Shang* (G#) mode. From a musical perspective, however, this is not necessary, since Earth-five is clearly meant to represent a lower-octave equivalent of the unmentioned Earth-ten.

But what does the Cosmogonic Sequence have to do with Chinese medicine? Indeed, the answer to this question is woven into the very fabric of meridian circulation. Figure 1.6 depicts the pentatonic scale as it appears within the wheel of the twelve meridians, the so-called Midnight-Midday circulation of energy. If we match each yin-yang pair of meridians with its respective phase, and each phase with its respective note, we find that the pentatonic scale begins with Water or D# in the Urinary Bladder meridian, and moves clockwise around the cycle to end with Earth or F# in the Spleen Meridian. Note that the two Fire phases occur at the longer intervals in the scale, i.e., between A# – C# and D# – F#, regardless of which mode the scale is sequenced in. If we order the scale according to the *Gong* mode as shown in Figure 1.6, the Sovereign Fire (Heart/Small Intestine) phase is "skipped over," i.e., left without a tone. We shall propose an explanation for this later.

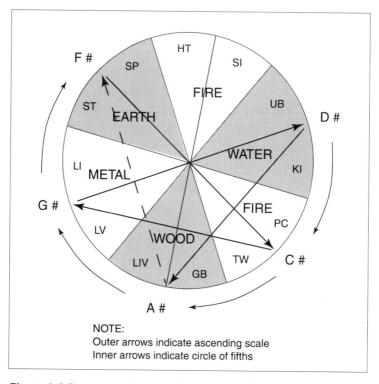

NOTE:
Outer arrows indicate ascending scale
Inner arrows indicate circle of fifths

Figure 1.6 Pentatonic Scale as it Appears in Midnight—Midday Sequence

Why does the scale appear to start at the Urinary Bladder? One of the present authors demonstrated how the energy "descends" into the body through the six meridian levels beginning with Tai Yang.[17] Furthermore, Chapter 76 of the *Ling Shu (Mystical Pivot)* identifies the Urinary Bladder as the beginning point of diurnal circulation:

> *At dawn, when the yin qi is exhausted, the yang qi will float out from the eyes; when the eyes open, the qi will ascend to the head, then descend along the neck to reach the Foot Tai Yang meridian, then descends along the back*

---

[17] Pirog, John, 1996, *Practical Application of Meridian Style Acupuncture*, p. 51.

to reach the Zhi Yin *point on the tip of the little toe.*

This makes the Urinary Bladder meridian of Foot Tai Yang the
ideal starting point for the Cosmogonic Sequence. But there is
another point in the meridian wheel that is even more important: the Gall Bladder meridian, situated in the "midnight"
position at the very bottom. We shall uncover the role this
meridian plays in Acutone therapy in Chapter 5.

For now, let us explore how the tones of the scale correlate with
the cardinal directions in the ancient five-phase compass diagram shown in Figure1.7. At first glance, it would appear that
the directions on this compass are upside down and backwards.
This is easily explained by the fact that the Chinese oriented
themselves toward the South (or more accurately, *opposite* the
North). To understand how the Chinese compass works, draw
an ordinary compass diagram, line up the cardinal points correctly and place it on the floor. Now look down on the compass
while facing south: the directions will line up exactly as in
Figure 1.7.

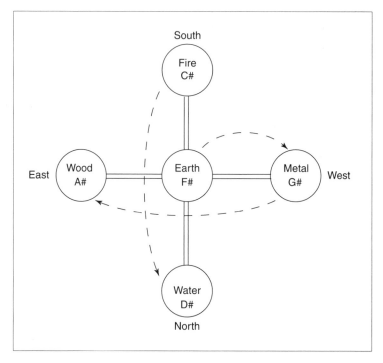

Figure 1.7 Five Phase "Compass" With Ascending Scale

Each direction in the Chinese compass is associated with a phase, which is in turn associated with a note on the pentatonic scale. If we ascend the scale in the *Gong* mode starting with F# (Figure 1.7), we will begin at the center of the compass (Earth), move across horizontally to G# (Metal/West), then across horizontally again to A# (Wood/East). We now must shift 90 degrees to move to C# (Fire/South) on the vertical axis, and then finally coming down to D# (Water/North). To return to F# we must shift 90 degrees again to return to the horizontal axis.

The movement thus described starts at the Center, moves from West to East, and then from South to North. This is the step-sequence of *evolution*, progressing upwards from the Earth where we stand to reach the circumpolar Heavens of the mystic North. But if we follow the Cosmogonic Sequence, however, we must move *down* the scale, and thus the circumambulatory sequence is reversed: first North to South, then East to West, finally ending at the Center (Figure 1.8). The Cosmogonic Sequence thus accords with the Southward-facing orientation of the Chinese cosmic compass, and with the percieved East-West transit of the celestial sphere. To move down the scale, therefore, is to follow the downward sequence of creation from Heaven to Earth. It is important to note that, whether one moves up or down the compass-scale, the shifts in axes occur at the longer musical intervals, i.e., between A# and C#, and between D# and F#.

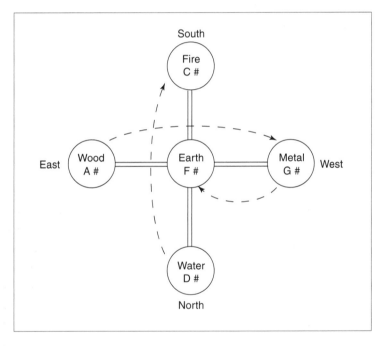

Figure 1.8 Five Phase "Compass" With Descending Scale

All this is further evidence that the early genesis of the five-phases was intimately linked to the pentatonic scale. In fact, the very term "five-phases" (*wu xing*) might better be translated as "five steps." The character *xing* (see Table 1.5) is a pictogram of two footprints, a left and a right. We know that ancient Chinese dance, choreographed to music from the pentatonic scale, was mapped out ritualistically in the five compass directions just described. It is quite possible that the five "phases" were originally derived from five repeating dance steps arranged in just such a fashion.

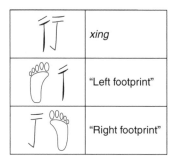

行	xing
	"Left footprint"
	"Right footprint"

Table 1.5 The Character Xing as Left and Right "Footprints"

Now let us work our way through the compass once more (Figure 1.9), this time ascending the scale by fifths. Beginning with F# (Earth/Center), we move up the compass to C# (Fire / South), then down to G# (Metal/West), then down to D# (Water/North), then up to A# (Wood/East). When we finally reach A#, we find there is no note on the scale with which it can form a perfect fifth. If we try to return from A# back to F# we will create an *augmented* fifth (a half-note higher than a perfect fifth), and if we try to go from A# to C# we will form a minor third. Remember that the perfect fifth is the one note in the octave that harmonizes perfectly with the fundamental. Each note in the five-tone scale seeks out and finds its perfect partner, but alas the poor A# has been left all alone!

The perfect fifth of A# is F-natural, and to find this tone our little A# will have to transcend the pentatonic scale altogether. How it accomplishes this we will save for Chapter 5.

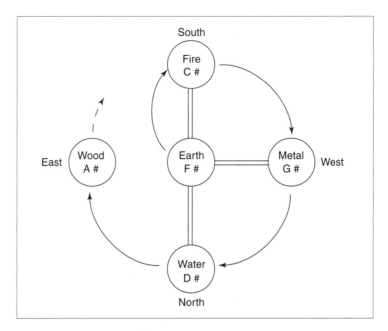

Figure 1.9 Five Phase "Compass" With Ascending Fifths

But we now have the explanation for the "missing tone" at the Sovereign Fire position (Heart/Small Intestine) of our meridian wheel (refer back to Figure 1.6). As you recall, each pair of meridians is linked together by a phase and its associated note. The Stomach-Spleen pair (Earth) are ruled by F#; if we go 180 degrees across the wheel we reach the Triple-Burner-Pericardium pair (Ministerial Fire) ruled by C#, thus forming a perfect fifth. Now let us continue to draw lines connecting each meridian pair by perfect fifths. We are left with a near-perfect pentagram. The "peak" of the pentagram points to the Wood phase, its two "legs" straddling the toneless Sovereign Fire phase. As the repository of the spirit (*shen*), Sovereign Fire is the pinnacle of human consciousness, and is thus capable of standing aloof from the five-pointed star of natural creation. Like the Emperor's name that could not be spoken, it is the tone that remains forever silent.

4. The Pentatonic Scale and Han Dynasty Acupuncture

While the association between the notes of the scale and the five-phases occurred in the late Zhou dynasty, it was in the Han dynasty, in the *Ling Shu (Mystical Pivot)*[18], that the pentatonic associations were extended to the five yin meridians and the five *zang*-viscera as laid out in Table 1.1. The *Ling Shu* even went so far as to map out different pitches for upper and lower parts of meridians, in a manner that seems to veritably invite some form of direct stimulation.[19] The connection between phase, organ, and note is so firmly established, in fact, that pentatonic notes sometimes appear as point names to indicate a role in the treatment of their phase-associated organ (Table 1.6).

---

[18] *Ling Shu (Mystical Pivot)* ch's. 64-65 (Liansheng Wu, Nelson and Andrew Qi Wu, transl.). These two chapters contain a series of twenty-five pentatonic notes with binomial designations, probably indicating pentatonic notes from five successive octaves. Although the association between the five notes and the Five-phases, five yin meridians, and five zang-organs as described in chapter 64 is clear enough, a more complex and ambiguous scheme is launched in chapter 65, where the tone associations do not match up with yang meridians in a manner consistent with the Five-phases. The task of reconciling these two schemes of tone-meridian association will have to be saved for future works by the authors.

[19] *Ling Shu (Mystical Pivot)* ch's 64-65 (Liansheng Wu, Nelson and Andrew Qi Wu, transl.); see note 14 above.

Tone	Character	Note	Organ	Acupuncture points with names containing note [20]	Alternate meaning
Gong		F#	Spleen	Sp 12, GV 26, UB 52, GV 4, P 8, K 3, Ht 6, Ki 19, SI 19, CV 4, CV 19	1. palace 2. temple 3. womb
Zhi		C#	Heart		
Shang		G#	Lung	Sp 5, Ki 17, LI 1, Lu 11	1. discuss: consult 2. merchant 3. name of Shang Dynasty
Yu		D#	Kidney	GV 18	feather; plume
Jue		A#	Liver	TW 20, GB 8	1. role; character 2. ancient three-legged wine cup 3. (as *Jiao*) horn, corner

Table 1.6 Tone/Character/Note/Organ/Points/Alternate Meanings

The note *Shang*, for example, which rules the Metal phase, appears in the names of Lu 11 (Lesser *Shang*), and LI 1 (*Shang Yang*). Both points belong to Metal and both are used in the treatment of Lung-related disorders such as loss of voice. Sp 5 (*Shang* Hill) is also a Metal point, and it too is indicated in the treatment of Lung disorders. Ki 17 (*Shang* Abode), located just

---

[20] The points listed in this table are taken from Wiseman, Ellis and Boss, *Grasping the Wind*, pp. 429-455.

above the navel, is used to treat the Large Intestine, a further connection with the Metal phase.

The character *Jue* (see Table 1.7), the musical tone for Wood, could easily have been corrupted into the character *Jiao*, meaning "horn" or "corner," and this may have taken place in some point names. GB 8 (*Shuai Jiao*) is usually translated as "Leading to the Corner." But given the location of this point above the ear, and its position on the Wood-associated Gall Bladder meridian, the original character may well have been *Jue*, in which case the intended meaning would have been "Leading to *Jue*." A similar rendering can be made for the point just beneath it, TW 20, "Grandson of *Jue*" (*Jue Sun*).

Chinese Character	Pinyin
	Jue
	Jiao
	Lu

Table 1.7 Jue/Jiao/Lu

The note *Gong*, the tone of Earth and its associated organ, the Spleen, can also mean "palace" and is usually rendered as such, e.g.: "Palace of Essence" (UB 52 and GV 4); "Palace of Toil" (Pc 8). But in at least some cases the use of *Gong* in point names indicates treatment of Earth-associated functions, as in the cases of Ki 19, (Stone *Gong*) located near the stomach, or Ki 3 (*Lu Gong*), the Earth point of the Kidney meridian. Since *Gong* is the quintessential note that defines pitch, we feel that *Ting Gong* (SI 19), the main local point for hearing disorders,

---

[21] Ellis, Wiseman and Boss, 1989, p. 142.

rendered by Wiseman and Ellis as "Auditory Palace,"[21] should be retranslated as "Auditory Pitch."

In addition to the names of tones themselves, there is evidence of other terms of musical significance in acupuncture point names. Some examples include *Xuan Zhong*, "Suspended Bell" (GB 39), a potential reference to the suspended chime-bells which were of supreme importance in Zhou dynasty ritual music, and *Kun Lun* (UB 60), the name of the mystical mountain where the first bamboo pitch-pipes were found. The cryptic character *Lu* (see Table 1.7), which appears in the names of three pitch-pipes (see Chapter 5), also appears in two of the names for Ki 3 (*Lu Gong* and Small *Lu*). The existence of these point names further emphasizes the influence of musicology on the genesis of acupuncture theory. Do we have any evidence, however, that Chinese music itself was used for healing purposes?

Most historical analysis on this subject has focused on *public* music, such as that played in ritual sacrifices. Performance of ritual music was designed to bring harmony between all those who were gathered to hear it, and therefore its healing function was social in nature rather than biological. Private music, however, was a different matter. In all cultures, soft music is used in a casual manner to promote an inner sense of well-being. Confucius was said to sing and play various instruments to calm his mind, and it is possible that some musical instruments, most likely flutes, played a role in Taoist introspection techniques. There can be no doubt that chanting and the music that necessarily accompanied it was essential to the healing rituals of the shaman-healers (*wu*), although we can at present only speculate on the form this ritual music would have taken.

Most likely, any healing done with musical instruments in historical Chinese practice reached the body of the patient through *oto-conduction*, i.e., through the sense of hearing. In the Acutone system outlined in the present book, we have designed a technique for reaching the body through *aqua-conduction*, i.e., by direct stimulation of the fluid medium within bodily tissues. This is accomplished by placing vibrating tuning forks directly on the skin. In this manner, the tone systems and meridian systems that were matched so meticulously in the classical texts can at last be combined in practice.

Although tuning forks themselves were not available to the ancient Chinese, they had in their possession a similar instrument: the chime-bell or *zhong*. Chinese chime-bells had no clapper; they were intoned by striking prescribed surface areas with wooden mallets. Some types of chime-bells were designed with a long stem or *yong*. One species of bell in particular, the *zeng*, was meant to be hand-held (Figure 1.10). Through experiments performed by Dean Lloyd, we have discovered that a bell-stem can conduct acoustic vibrations in much the same way as the stem of a tuning fork. Constructed in the right size, shape, and frequency specifications, a set of *zeng* could be used in Acutone treatment in a manner similar to the techniques prescribed in this book for tuning forks.

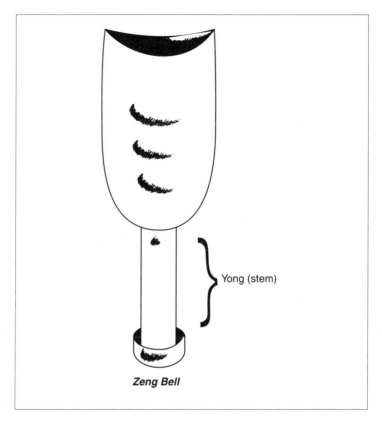

Yong (stem)

Zeng Bell

Figure 1.10 Zeng Bell

While the early Zhou dynasty placed many restrictions on the ownership and use of such bells, these restrictions were gradually relaxed in the Late Zhou and early Han Dynasties. It is conceivable that medically useful *zeng* bells were available to resourceful physicians. Although we can present no proof that bells were used in any systematic fashion in later Chinese medicine, the possibility of such application cannot be ruled out. In any case, the modern availability of tuning forks allow us to finally fill in this apparent void in the application of Han Dynasty medical theory.

Chapter II

Getting Started With Acutone Therapy

1. Wave Theory and the Tao

Perhaps the most pivotal emphasis of Chinese natural philosophy is the study of the laws of *change*. The ancient sages taught that all things in the temporal universe are subject to orderly changes that include birth, growth, decay, and ultimately regeneration. But it was the cyclical nature of change that most captured the imagination of the Chinese mystics: changes in nature seemed to oscillate between two polar extremes. The sun could only climb so far in the heavens before it began to descend, and once it had reached its nadir it began to climb yet again. The summer could only become so hot before it began to cool, and the winter could only become so cold before it began to warm. Thus was born the theory of yin and yang.

The ancients saw the ripples and waves of moving water as the most graphic representation of the constant flux between yin and yang. The study of waves is of particular interest in the present discussion, since sound is a form of energy that moves in waves of pressure displacement. When sound resonates through a body of fixed dimension such as a guitar box, a tuning fork, or the fluid in a human cell, *stationary waves* are produced.

In a stationary wave, energy is transmitted from point to point through a vibrating medium without movement of the medium as a whole in the direction of the wave. Ocean waves are examples of stationary waves; they only *appear* to move toward the shore. In fact, as any surfer knows, the water at the crest is traveling toward the shore while the water at the trough is traveling away from the shore, and there is no forward movement of the water as a whole. Likewise, acoustic waves travel from point to point through the air without movement of the air as a whole in the direction of the propagation of sound.

Figure 2.1 shows a simple stationary wave. The straight line indicates normal pressure, and the curved line depicts the pressure displacement. The peak of the wave (A) indicates maximum increase in pressure while the trough (B) depicts maximum decrease in pressure. The two points A' and B' represent the points of maximum pressure displacement. They are referred to as *antinodes*. Points (C) and (D) are referred to as *nodes*; they are the points of minimum pressure displacement. So long as the frequency remains constant, the nodes and antinodes in a stationary wave will not move, although the displacement wave itself will constantly shift up and down.

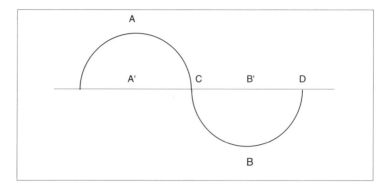

Figure 2.1 Wave Showing Node/Antinode

The movement of a stationary wave can best be illustrated by a swinging pendulum (Figure 2.2). The extreme ends of the swing represent the antinodes, the points where the pendulum slows down and reverses direction. The pendulum is moving fastest as it passes through the perpendicular point of balance in the center. In the same manner, the pressure changes in a stationary wave must slow down and reverse "direction" at its antinodes. The wave is theoretically moving fastest when the antinodes reach the straight line in Figure 2.1, where the pressure displacement is zero. At the nodes, however, no change in pressure takes place.

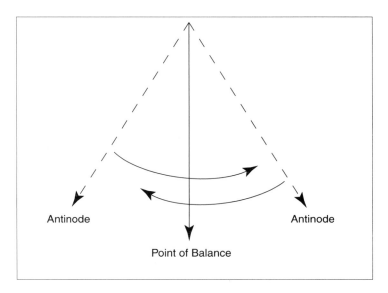

Figure 2.2 Pendulum Showing Node/Antinode

If we superimpose a circle over our wave diagram (Figure 2.3), we have the famous *tai qi* symbol, the ancient diagram that depicted the cyclical oscillation of yin and yang. Note that the two inner circles, which were meant to represent yin being born within yang and vice versa, are placed at the antinodes of the stationary wave—*the points where the wave "motion" reverses direction*. In effect, the antinodes of a wave represent the points where the mysterious inter-transformation of yin and yang take place.

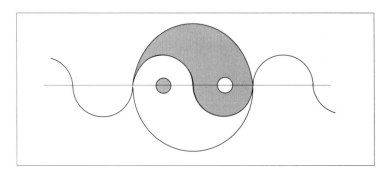

Figure 2.3 Wave in Yin Yang symbol

In our own civilization, wave theory is the dry stuff of physics classes. But to the ancient Chinese the wave was a living entity, constantly shaping the universe as a river shapes the surrounding earth. The wave represented the creative powers of *qi*, the ability of energy to give shape to form. The frequency of a wave was all-important, since it allowed the mystic to calculate the position of the antinode—the point where yin would transform into yang. To control frequency was to control life—*thus, music was the ultimate magic.*

In this sense, all cycles in nature can be seen as wave forms with their own characteristic nodes and antinodes. In the daily cycle, the antinodes are at the extremes of light and dark, represented by noon and midnight respectively. In the yearly cycle, the antinodes correspond with the solstices. In each case, the antinodes are the points where yin and yang reach their extremes and begin to change back into their opposites. Not surprisingly, the two most important rituals in the ancient Chinese calendar, the rituals of heaven and earth, took place at the solstices.

While ancient Chinese philosophers may have had a symbolic understanding of nodes and frequency, ancient Chinese musicians had to work out the practical effects of these phenomena when they designed musical instruments. The most sophisticated instruments in the ancient Chinese ritual ensemble were the two-tone chime-bells or *zhong* that became popular in the Eastern Zhou Dynasty (Figure 2.4). These unique bells were designed with almond-shaped cross-sections and curved bottoms. Because of this peculiar shape, they were capable of emitting two distinct tones, depending on whether the bell was struck in the center (*Zheng Gu* tone) or on the sides (*Ce Gu* tone). It is important to note that these two tones were a major or minor third apart. As we saw in Chapter 1, the minor third is the longer interval occurring between the tones *Jue—Zhi* and *Yu—Gong*, while the major third plays a critical role in the twelve-meridian Acutone technique we will develop in Chapter 6.

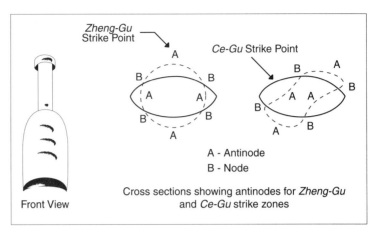

Figure 2.4 Zheng Bell Showing Node/Antinode

The inner surfaces of two-tone bells were modeled to create areas of different thickness in the walls. These differences served to demarcate the respective strike zones. Figure 2.4 shows a cross-section of a bell with a comparison of the node-antinode distribution patterns for the two tones. As can be seen from the diagram, the centers of the thinner walls coincide with the antinodes of the *Zheng Gu* tone, while these same zones coincide with the nodes of the *Ce Gu* tone.[22] Clearly, there was an empirical, if not theoretical, understanding of the effects of nodes and antinodes in the creation of these bells.

Nodes and antinodes can be seen in the design of the body's meridian system.[23] According to traditional circulation theory, the meridian energy moves in a complete circle between the head, chest, and extremities. The energy moves fastest as it passes through the head and chest, while at the hands and feet, it slows down, reverses direction and returns again to the head and chest (Figure 2.5). The *jing*-well points at the hands and feet therefore represent the "antinodes" of the meridian circulation—the end points of the body's own "pendulum swing." The radial pulse itself is a stationary wave and the different

---

[22] Von Falkenhausen, p. 80-84.

[23] Pirog, *Practical Application of Meridian Style Acupuncture*, 1996, p.70-72.

pulse qualities such as slippery, wiry, etc., are dependent in part on the overlap of nodes and antinodes formed by various partials.

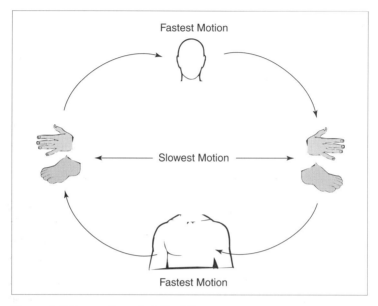

Figure 2.5 Energy Speed of Meridians

There are nodes and antinodes in a tuning fork as well (see Figure 2.6). So long as the tuning fork is struck with a blunt object, the antinodes occur at the tips of the prongs and the bottom of the curve, where the stem attaches. This means that the stem of the tuning fork is actually vibrating *up and down*, the same motion as the lift-and-thrust movement of an acupuncture needle. This vibratory property makes the tuning fork uniquely suited for stimulation of acupuncture points.

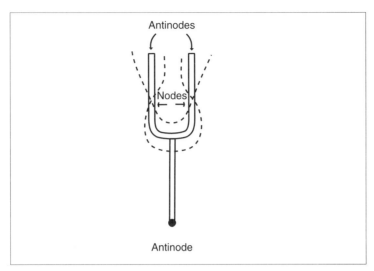

Figure 2.6 Tuning fork Showing Node/Antinode

In most musical instruments, stationary waves are complicated by the production of *partials*. Partial tones are higher frequencies that occur mixed together with the fundamental tone; they are discernible to the musically sensitive ear when any single note is played. Each musical instrument possesses its own unique recipe of partials, and these are responsible for the instrument's characteristic sound quality or timber. Among Western musical instruments, the violin generates the greatest number of partials, while the flute has the fewest (Figure 2.7). The tone of a tuning fork is almost pure, having practically no partials at all.

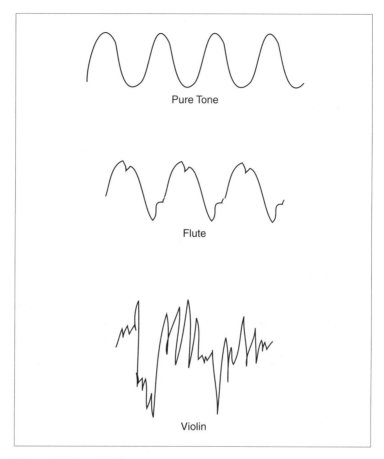

Figure 2.7 Sound Waves

Pure tones are virtually absent in nature. Whether we are listening to music, the splashing of waves, or the hum of traffic, our ears are constantly exposed to a complex mix of partial frequencies. Because it is so rarely experienced, the pure tone emitted by the tuning fork provides a unique stimulus that the body cannot easily ignore, and this makes it an ideal instrument for Acutone therapy.

The relationship of partial frequencies to the fundamental tone is defined by the harmonic series we encountered in Chapter 1. As can be seen in Figure 2.8, the first partial occurs at the second harmonic, this frequency being the higher octave of the fundamental frequency. The subsequent partials form the fifth, the next octave, the major third, and so on. To the ears of the musical sages, it sounded as if each individual tone had an inherent "desire" to create its higher octave and its upper fifth. This concept is critical to the understanding of Acutone theory; we will return to it in Chapter 6.

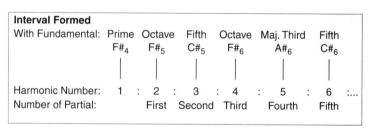

Figure 2.8 Interval Harmonic Relationship

2. Getting To Know The Tuning Forks

Looking for a convenient device to tune his lute, John Shore, a trumpeter for Handel, invented the tuning fork in the early 18th Century.[24] Because of the tuning fork's convenience and purity of tone, it has long been popular as a tuning instrument, although more recently it has been replaced by electronic devices.

A standard set of tuning forks will contain a full chromatic scale of thirteen forks beginning with middle C. This is usually written as "C_4" in American standard notation and C^1 on German tuning forks (Table 2.1). The tuning forks are set to *equal temperament*, a scale system that was originally designed for keyboard instruments such as the harpsichord and the piano. In an equally tempered chromatic scale, the frequencies of all tones are mathematically adjusted to allow easier transposition of keys. The tempered scale is a musical compromise, since the notes so produced will be slightly out of tune with

---

24 Wood, p. 146.

each other. The use of a tempered scale does not interfere with the effectiveness of Acutone work, since many sets of Chinese chime-bells were tempered as well. [25]

German	American
C^1	C_4
C^{is}	$C\#_4$
D^1	D_4
D^{is}	$D\#_4$
E^1	E_4
F^1	F_4
F^{is}	$F\#_4$
G^1	G_4
G^{is}	$G\#_4$
A^1	A_4
B^1	B^b $(A\#_4)$
h^1	B_4
C^2	C_5

Table 2.1 Comparison of German and American Standard Notation

A tuning fork is essentially a vibrating bar with two nodes (Figure 2.6). By bending the bar, the nodes come closer together. The frequency of the tuning fork's fundamental is based on the length of the prongs, with the lower pitches requiring longer prongs and vice versa. As we explained earlier, the stem of the tuning fork is placed at the peak of the central antinode, the other two antinodes occurring at the tips of the prongs. This means that the two prongs of the tuning fork will vibrate *transversely*, while the stem vibrates *up and down*. This allows the instrument to be held at its stem without dulling the vibration.

So long as the tuning fork is struck with a blunt object or the two prongs pinched off between the fingers, the tone emitted will be nearly pure. It can be heard as a soft hum barely per-

---

25 Von Falkenhausen, p. 92 (see also Appendix I).

ceptible unless the prongs are held close to the ear. If struck against a hard object, the tuning fork will generate a series of partials audible as a high-pitched ringing.

For the purposes of the Acutone techniques used in this book, only the pure tone or fundamental is utilized, and the ringing of partials should be carefully avoided. This will require a little bit of practice. If possible, you should try to sound the tuning fork by striking it on or near your own body, or by pinching the prongs between your fingers. This will help to reverberate your own qi into the instrument. If this proves too painful or difficult, you can substitute a handball (cut in half) or a rubber heel.

Holding the stem loosely between the thumb and forefinger, gently tap the fork at the midpoint of the prong (Figure 2.9). If you are sounding the tuning fork by striking against your own body, use the stretched tendons just above the bent knee in the approximate area of Sp 10 or St 34, or on the elbow near TW 10, or on the thenar eminence at Lu 10. You can get a fairly strong resonance by tapping the fork gently against the point and allowing it to bounce back quickly on its own. In order to accomplish this the stem must be held quite loosely.

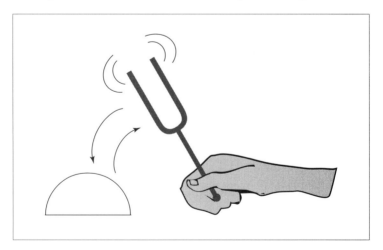

Figure 2.9 Striking Fork on Sliced Handball

When left to vibrate in the open air, the sound emitted by a tuning fork is barely audible. This is because the vibrating prongs are quite narrow, allowing the surrounding air molecules to easily slide around their edges and thus avoid picking up the vibration. If the tuning fork is placed between two bricks, the loudness increases slightly because the air between the bricks is forced into contact with the vibrating prongs and greater pressure changes are generated.

But if the stem of the fork is held firmly against a wall, the tone becomes much louder, capable of being heard throughout the room. This is called a *forced frequency*. The up-and-down vibration of the stem forces the acoustic energy of the fork into the molecules of the wall, which in turn communicates the frequency to the surrounding air. Because the wall is much larger than the prongs of the fork, the air cannot slip over its edges, and much higher pressure changes are generated. This increased pressure requires greater energy output, and so the sound of the fork will die away much more quickly than if left to vibrate in the open air.

The volume of the tone will be increased even further if it matches the *natural frequency* of the room itself. The natural frequency of an object is the wavelength produced by its size and shape, as well as the resonance properties of the material it is made of. As we have just seen, the differences in frequency between tuning forks is based on the length of their prongs. This length establishes a fixed distance between nodes and antinodes and therefore creates a specific natural frequency.

In the case of pitch-pipes (see Chapter 1), the natural frequency is set by the length and width of the column of vibrating air inside the pipe. As we have seen, different sized pitch-pipes will produce different tones. As we learned in Chapter 1, the natural frequency of the earth itself was the *Huang Zhong* tone, and the pitch-pipe that produced it was made the basis of all

---

[26] Von Falkenhausen, p. 315.

length, weight, and volumetric measurement in ancient China, much like our modern meter. [26]

This being the case, we might surmise that the *Huang Zhong* was particularly important in the design of buildings, where it must have been employed by *Feng Shui* practitioners to establish the dimensions of doorways, windows, walls, and ceilings. We may even speculate that the true goal of *Feng Shui* was to produce natural frequencies in an edifice that would harmonize its occupants with each other and with the surrounding geography.

In effect, the building in which you live or work is a giant musical instrument. The walls in each room and the air contained inside them all have their own natural frequencies. When the frequency of a tuning fork matches the natural frequency of the object it is vibrating, *resonance* is said to occur, and the tone will be much louder.

Unfortunately, the deeper teachings of *Feng Shui* are mostly lost, and this ancient science has degenerated into a kind of New Age interior design. You must use your intuition to determine the suitability of a building or treatment room for Acutone. But even if you find that a room's natural frequencies are not harmonious with you, it is possible to impose new frequencies through the techniques described below.

3. Clearing the Frequencies of the Treatment Room

Modern man spends much of his time fighting the season. We curse the leaves for littering our lawn, and then we curse the snow for accumulating on our driveway. Independent of the physical effects of the weather itself, this continuous sense of anti-seasonal combat is bound to take its toll on our health. The techniques presented in this section are designed to produce a sense of harmony between our inner being and the space surrounding us, so that the beauty and vitality of the changing seasons can be used to enhance the vitality rather than struggle against it.

To accomplish this, we always begin Acutone therapy by "clearing the room." Dean Lloyd developed this method after teaching an outdoor seminar one weekend. He gathered the forty people present into a circular chorus, placing the "patient" in the center. He rang the tuning fork of the requisite tone in the ear of each member of the chorus. One by one, all the voices would begin to hum that tone. The whole area suddenly came alive with the chosen frequency, surrounding the patient with a wall of sound.

It is important to understand that the bodily energies are impacted by frequencies applied *outside* as well as inside. A vibrating tuning fork affects the body in two ways. When its stem is pressed against an acupuncture point, its fundamental is introduced directly into the body through the fluid medium in the cells. But the tuning fork also affects the body *from the outside*, since the oscillating prongs communicate their frequency to the surrounding air (Figure 2.10A). This is a vital concept, since Chinese medicine is founded on the belief that energies within the body are profoundly affected by the energies surrounding it. "Evil qi" such as wind, cold, and damp can be thought of in the present context as dissonant frequencies that disrupt the harmony of the organism with which they come in contact.

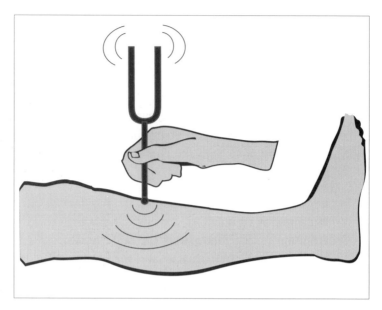

Figure 2.10A Frequency transferred to the Body

If we can purify the frequencies of the seasonal energies in the treatment room, they are less likely to imbalance the energies of the patient and the practitioner. To do this, *the room should be cleared of all frequencies except for the one that is most appropriate for the season*. The room should be cleared at the beginning of each treatment day, as well as before and after each treatment.

In most cases, the room is cleared by the tone that matches the current season (see Table 1.1). The simplest method is to vibrate the appropriate tuning fork against the walls of the room, perhaps including the treatment Table. The stem of the fork must be pressed quickly and tightly against the wall to avoid rattling, and it should be held in place until the sound becomes inaudible (Figure 2.10B). Wooden walls will resonate much better than stone walls, although the volume of the tone is not necessarily as important as its frequency. You may put your finger between the tuning fork and the wall to help buffer the vibration from the initial contact (Figure 2.10C).

Figure 2.10B Clearing Room With Direct Contact

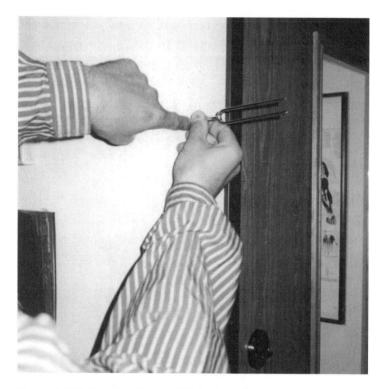

Figure 2.10C Clearing Room With Indirect Contact

How does one know which season is current? The ancient Chinese had many overlapping systems for determining seasons, some of them quite complex. In addition, the number and types of seasons vary considerably in different parts of the world, and pure Chinese models might not fit every locale. For the purposes of clearing a room, we recommend that you use your own instinctive "seasonal sense" to decide which tone is appropriate, rather than trying to work it out through a calendar. During the warm summer months, for example, the obvious choice is C#, the tone of the Fire phase, while on cold winter days you will likely use D#, the tone for Water.

The tone of the Earth phase, F#, is usually said to correlate with the damp muggy period between late summer and early fall. Not all climates have this season. But the Earth frequency can also be used *during any inter-seasonal period* when the weather seems to oscillate between the former season and the later, as in Midwest springs when the weather fluctuates from cold to warm to cold again. The Earth tone can also be used during any period when highly "un-seasonal" weather is present, as in the case of very cold days in the middle of the summer. This is because Earth occupies the central harmonizing position in the five-phase system, capable of bringing the human frequencies into balance during any climatic extreme.

Although the frequencies produced by the above technique may appear to quickly die out, they actually leave a lasting impression on the matter-energy patterns in the room. Such patterns can be graphically demonstrated through a Chladni plate (Figure 2.11). This is a thin steel plate covered evenly with a fine dusting of sand. When a violin bow is drawn across the edge of the plate, the vibrations will arrange the sand in line patterns that coincide with the nodes of the stationary wave.

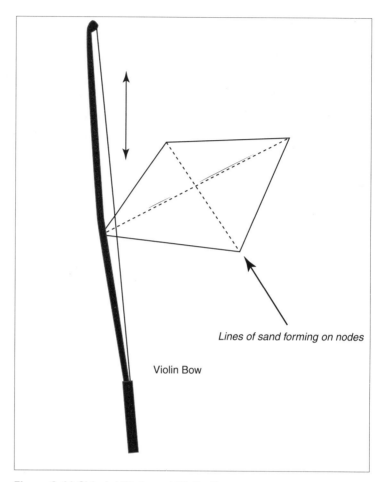

Lines of sand forming on nodes

Violin Bow

Figure 2.11 Chladni Plate and Violin Bow

In the same manner, patterns of nodes and antinodes can fill walls of a treatment room, leftover vestiges of the various frequencies brought into that room by conversations, music, and background noise. By clearing the room at the beginning of the day and before each treatment, these extraneous frequency patterns will be brushed aside and replaced with a pure tone that lines up perfectly with the seasonal energies. Thus, anyone who enters the room will begin to be healed.

4. The Resonance Bell

One of the best methods for clearing a room is through the use of a portable instrument invented by Dean Lloyd called the *Resonance Bell*. This is a U-shaped box made of rosewood with a circular hole cut on the flat side (Figure 2.12). On one end there is a small wooden bar with two notches for holding tuning forks.

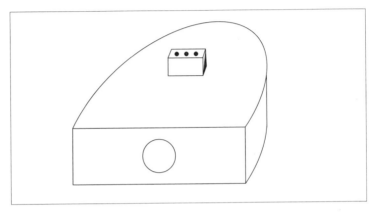

Figure 2.12 Resonance Bell

To use the Resonance Bell, take two tuning forks of the same frequency (you will need to keep two identical sets of tuning forks for this) and place them in the notches of the wooden bar. They must be held in place with your thumb while the rest of your hand grips the body of the Bell. Using the thumb and fore-finger of the opposite hand, pinch together the prongs of one of the tuning forks. As the tone begins to fade, pinch the other tuning fork. By alternately pinching one tuning fork then the other, a sustained pure tone can be produced.

You may also use a single tuning fork in the Resonance Bell. Pluck the end prongs to start the tone and pluck it again before the sound dies.

The tone is emitted through the instrument's hole. In order to direct the frequency, simply point the instrument in the direction where you want the sound to go. In room clearing, you can point the Bell in the four cardinal directions, or simply sweep it around the room (Figure 2.13A). This technique can also be used when the Resonance Bell is facing a curtain or partition that cannot produce a sound with direct contact of the tuning fork. If the room has been cleared, you may also augment the treatment space by using the Resonance Bell closer to the patient—approximately one to two feet away—surrounding the body (Figure 2.13B). We will encounter other uses for the Resonance Bell later in this book. See Appendix D for retail sources for the Resonance Bell.

Figure 2.13A Clearing Room With Resonance Bell

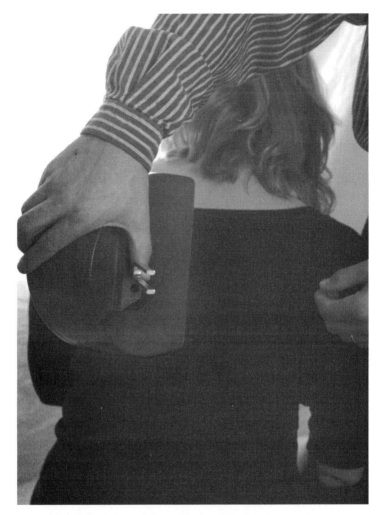

Figure 2.13B Resonance Bell Used in Treatment

5. Other Methods for Room Clearing

In his practice, Dean Lloyd uses a number of additional techniques for clearing a room. Here are just a few of them:

- *Use the instrument of the phase belonging to the season* (see Table 1.1). During the summer, for example, a stringed instrument such as a violin can be used. Always play the pitch of the season. In the case of summer, for example, you would play C#. The winter instrument is the drum. If it is not possible to tune the drum to D#, simply introduce this tone into the walls with a D# tuning fork as described above, and afterwards any drum can be played to make the effect complete. Still another method is beat the drum at a rate of 72.4 beats per minute (1.207 Hz); this is a frequency eight octaves below D#$_4$. A metronome can be set to obtain the right beat.

- *Use yourself as the clearing instrument*. After listening to the seasonal tone on a tuning fork, hum the frequency aloud or silently as you touch the wall for several seconds.

- *Use the frequency of the hour based on the Chinese clock.* There may be circumstances when the frequency of the hour appears to be stronger than the frequency of the season. When this happens, you may find it difficult to "hear" or attune to the seasonal tone. In such cases you will have to choose the appropriate note from the twelve-hour Chinese clock (Figure 5.1). Simply pick the note that matches the hour. Bear in mind that the twelve-hour "clock" is based on "sundial time," not conventional civil time. To use it accurately, you will need to subtract one hour during daylight savings time and make further adjustments depending on your office location and time of year (see Appendix C).

- *Use F-natural.* There may be times when it will become necessary to clear away all frequencies in a room. Due to interference from the emotionality of people who have occupied the room, or because of imbalanced energy from natural events such as solar eclipses, the appropriate frequencies may not "stick." In this case, you must start from scratch and erase all other sounds. The frequency that can best accomplish this is F-natural, the fundamental tone of the twelve-tone color wheel (see Chapter 5). This frequency corresponds with the transition from the visible to the invisible spectrum of light. By intoning it you will have the effect of clearing away all other frequencies in the room, so that any tone that is later played will theoretically take place in a neutral environment.

6. Manipulation Techniques

As we explained in our introduction, tuning forks are used on the body to stimulate meridians and points in much the same way that teishins are used in modern Japan. A *teishin* is a blunt "needle" which comes in various sizes, shapes and materials (Figure 2.14). They are a popular means of stimulating points without breaking the skin. Although these instruments may look somewhat crude at first glance, their effectiveness depends on very delicate manipulation techniques and special point selection schemes. There are many Teishin masters in modern Japan who use this instrument as the sole treatment tool in their practice. Compare the likeness of the tuning fork and the teishin (Figure 2.14).

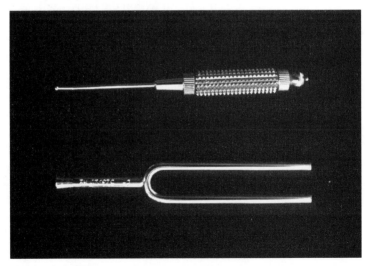

Figure 2.14 Teishin Compared to Tuning Fork

Unlike Teishins, however, the tuning fork is a *vibrating* instrument. Its therapeutic effect depends more on the appropriate selection of frequency than on manipulation technique as such. While most of this present volume is concerned with the correct application of frequency, optimum results will require some skill at manipulation as well.

In general, acupuncture and teishin techniques are divided into those that *supplement* and those that *drain*. Put simply, supplementation means an augmentation of the quantity of energy in a particular point, meridian or region, while drainage means a reduction of energy in the same manner. Supplementation is used in points or meridians that are deficient or lacking in right qi (*zheng qi*), the body's own constitutional energy. Drainage is undertaken when there is excess, usually due to a build-up of evil qi (*xie qi*)—energy that does not belong in the body. Sometimes this excess comes from the outside environment, in which case it is classified according to a climatic extreme such as wind, cold, or damp. In some cases, excess qi builds up as a result of blocked circulation within the body itself, examples of which include phlegm, digestate stagnation, and blood stasis.

As a general rule, supplementation requires *milder* stimulus, while drainage requires *stronger* stimulus. This is because supplementation is an attempt to gently prod the body into an increase in physiological function. Drainage requires slightly more force since it is an attempt to assist the body in fighting off something that does not belong. Most illness is a mixture of excess and deficiency and a comprehensive treatment will often include a mixture of both supplementation and drainage.

In order to effect supplementation and drainage with tuning forks, we have adopted some of the techniques used with acupuncture (Table 2.2). The stem of the tuning fork should be used like the handle of a needle or teishin. It is usually held between the thumb and index and middle fingers of the right hand. You will need to be careful not to touch the vibrating prongs, because this will kill the frequency.

Supplement	Drain
Tuning fork should be vibrating softly	Tuning fork should be vibrating loudly
"Insert" slowly	"Insert" rapidly
Press lightly (i.e., "superficial insertion")	Press firmly (i.e., "deep insertion")
Withdraw after vibration is weak or gone	Withdraw when vibration is still strong
Withdraw rapidly	Withdraw slowly
Insert on exhalation, withdraw on inhalation	Insert on inhalation, withdraw on exhilation
Close "hole"	Leave "hole" open
Angle or stroke in direction of meridian	Angle or stroke against meridian

Table 2.2 Supplementation vs. Drainage Techniques

Since the tuning fork affects the energy both outside the body as well as inside, the treatment will actually begin when the fork is first struck. When you "insert" a tuning fork into a point, it should be advanced in a straight line from a starting point of six inches to one foot away from the point. Likewise, when it is withdrawn it should be withdrawn in a straight line for the same distance.

For supplementation, advance the stem of the tuning fork slowly until it reaches the skin, then press very gently. Hold it still until the vibration is no longer perceptible, and then quickly but gently withdraw the stem while simultaneously closing the "hole" with the opposite finger. If one hand is being used, the "hole" can be closed with the middle finger while the thumb and index finger pull the stem from the skin. There is, of course, no actual "hole", as there might be if an acupuncture needle were inserted, but the pressure of the finger on the skin will create a node in the wave pattern introduced at that point, much like a finger pressed against a vibrating string (Figure 2.15).

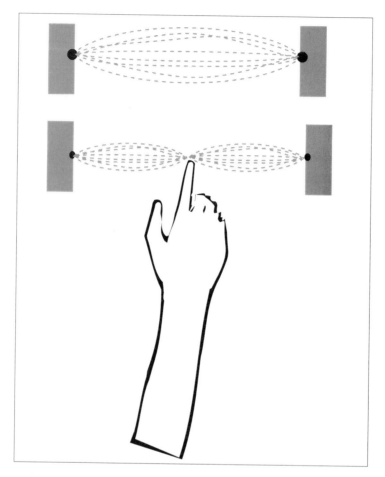

Figure 2.15 Creation of Node on a Vibrating String

In conventional acupuncture, the hole is closed to prevent the escape of right qi through the punctured skin. In Acutone, energy takes the form of *vibration*. In the experiment on the Chladni plates described above, the sand tended to collect along the node lines of the plate where the *least* vibration occurred. In contrast, it was scattered away from the antinodes of the plate where there was the *greatest* vibration. In the same manner, we press our finger on the point in order to form a node, thus preventing any scattering of qi caused by the vibration just introduced there.

To drain energy, the above formula is reversed. The tuning fork stem is introduced quickly into the point, it is pressed slightly harder (though not too hard), and withdrawn slowly while the tuning fork is still vibrating. The "hole" is left open in order to maintain the antinode formed at the point (remember that the stem of the tuning fork is at the central antinode of the fork itself).

Most acupuncturists believe that the needle should be inserted during exhalation for supplementation and inhalation for drainage. The breath cycle is yet another wave-form in the human body, with the two antinodes occurring when the lungs are full (end of inhalation) and empty (end of exhalation). During inhalation, the pressure increases tend to push the meridian energy toward the outside of the body, while exhalation reduces the pressure and make it easier for energy to be drawn into the body.

Supplementation is a process of drawing energy *into* the body; therefore, to supplement, you must "insert" the fork *as the patient is exhaling*. This allows the frequency to follow the qi into the body. This technique can best be learned by practicing on the abdomen. To supplement, push the stem inward as the abdomen falls, and pull outward as the abdomen rises. Drainage is a process of drawing the energy *out* of the body, so the above technique is reversed, i.e., insert during inhalation, and withdraw during exhalation.

The other details of insertion and withdrawal are not quite as important. To supplement, for example, you should insert in the direction of the flow of the meridian qi; in the opposite direction to drain. The *Nei Jing* offers at least two different schemes of meridian circulation, however, and there are differences of opinion as to which one is most important.[27] It is also difficult to follow this technique when an additional fork is used on a nearby point.

---

[27] Pirog, *Practical Application of Meridian Style Acupuncture*, 1996, p. 33-36

Most of the time, the tuning fork frequencies are conducted through body fluids and are barely perceptible to the patient. But when a tuning fork is pressed firmly over a bone, the tone vibrates very intensely through the bone matrix and the effect will be felt rather intensely by the patient. The resonating properties of bones are well known to modern medicine. In modern Western medicine, tuning forks are resonated against bones as a test for hidden fractures.

Since strong stimulus tends to drain, we recommend you do not introduce frequencies directly into large bones unless there is strong excess that needs to be drained at the bone level (see below). If a selected acupuncture point happens to be located over a bone, as is the case with points located on the scalp or sternum, you can soften the vibration by sending the frequencies through your own finger. Place the index finger or thumb of the opposite hand on the point and then place the tuning fork stem over the finger nail (Figure 2.16). The vibration will be carried into the point without producing any unwanted resonance. If you want to close the "hole" in this technique, simply leave the finger on the point after withdrawing the fork. Likewise, if you want to leave the hole open, withdraw the finger and tuning fork in tandem.

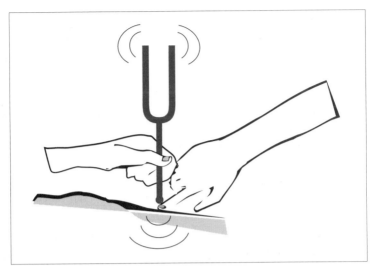

Figure 2.16 Fork Closing Hole With Finger

The tuning fork stimulus need not be restricted to stimulus of a single point. It is possible to use the tuning forks over an entire meridian or across a large body surface like the posterior shoulders. Here are just a few techniques that you might find useful:

• *Stroking:* Stroke the stem of the tuning fork gently over a meridian (Figure 2.17). To supplement, press lightly, stroke in the direction of the meridian; to drain, press more firmly and stroke against the direction of the meridian.

• *Trilling:* Flip the angle of the stem forward each time as you press against a series of points. Press softer to supplement, harder to drain (Figure 2.18).

For additional techniques, see Chapter 8, "Auxiliary Techniques."

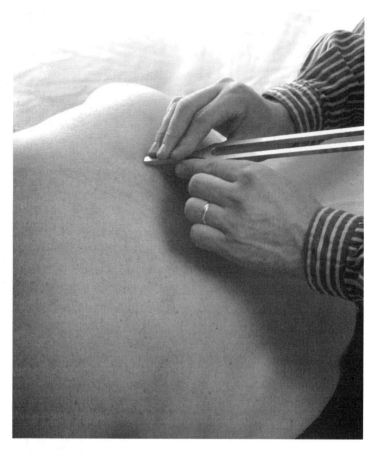

Figure 2.17 Tuning Fork Using Stroking Technique

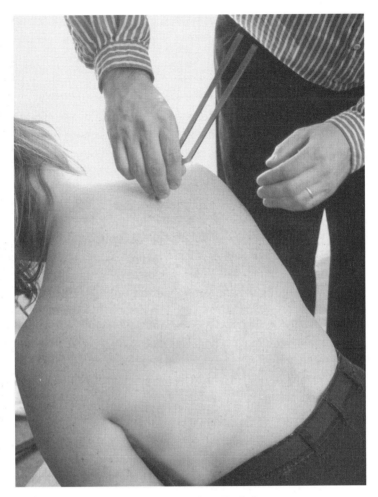

Figure 2.18 Tuning Fork Using Trilling Technique

7. Local Treatment

Local treatment refers to the treatment of points or regions that are in the immediate vicinity of the symptoms being addressed. Points on the head are local for vertigo; points on the shoulder are local for shoulder pain, points on the abdomen are local for nausea, and so on. The local treatment principles outlined below can be used with either the five-phase or twelve-meridian Acutone systems that are described later (chapters 4 and 6

61

respectively). Furthermore, the same techniques can be applied to any form of local points, whether they be anatomically located meridian points (e.g. LI 15 for shoulder pain, UB 52 for back pain) or empirical points. Examples of empirical points include *ashi* points, located according to tenderness on pressure, and *kori*, gum-like hard spots in muscle and connective tissue.

Local points are usually drained, although supplementation or mixed supplementation and drainage might be necessary in constitutionally weaker patients or in areas where the symptoms are very chronic and the local tissues have deteriorated. You may use any of the manipulation techniques described in the preceding section or in Chapter 8. In general, the stimulus used in treating local points is somewhat stronger than the stimulus used in the root treatment we will describe in Chapter 4.

The rule is simple: *only one tuning fork can be used at one time on any one local point.* The tuning fork is selected from one of the five notes of the Chinese pentatonic scale. You may use one of four basic criteria to determine which of the five tones is appropriate.

Method 1. Select the Tone According To External Pathogen

This method is easiest when a single pathogen can be clearly identified. If multiple pathogens are present, as in the case of "wind-cold-damp" you should select the tone of the pathogen that appears most dominant, or switch to methods 2 or 3 below.

Wind: A# or G#

Internal wind produces spasm and tremors in the muscles, and is therefore associated with the Wood phase and its tone, A#. *External* wind is more closely associated with Metal, and might respond better to G#. External wind produces sudden onset of pain that moves quickly from one site to another, often after exposure to drafts. There may be a strong floating pulse and in severe cases, chills and fever.

Damp: F#

Damp is ruled by the Earth phase and is controlled by F#. It causes chronic dull aching with a sensation of heaviness, as well as tightness and crackling noises in the joints. It worsens when the weather is rainy or humid. The pulse is slippery and the tongue coat greasy.

Cold: D#

Cold is associated with the Water phase and its tone, D#. It causes severe pain and palpable coldness in the affected region, and is worse in winter and cold weather. The pulse may be slow or tight, and the tongue tends to be pale and swollen with a glossy white coat.

Heat: C#

Heat is ruled by the Fire phase and C#. It produces localized redness, swelling, and pain with palpable heat. Rheumatoid arthritis in younger people often has this appearance. Heat can also produce bright red skin lesions. The pulse is fast and the tongue is red with a yellow coat.

Method 2: Select the Tone According To Affected Tissue

This method is most appropriate when there is a single local tissue that can be identified as the source of the symptom. If several tissues are involved, it is best to begin by treating the more superficial problems first (e.g., skin and capillaries), and then working progressively into the deeper layers (e.g., sinew and bone). This method is not necessarily at odds with method #1, since pathogens tend to gravitate to the tissue ruled by their phase. The redness and swelling of heat, for example, is caused by a dilation of the capillaries, and dampness tends to be a condition of the flesh.

Skin: G#

The skin is ruled by the Metal phase and its tone is G#. This tone works best for superficial numbness and pain, such as that caused by peripheral neuropathies. It may also be used for some skin diseases, particularly when these occur suddenly, as in the case of hives, or when the lesions are dry and exfoliating, as in certain forms of eczema. Not all skin problems are Metal, however. Hot, red, swollen lesions tend to involve the capillaries (C#), while weeping lesions might be the result of pathogenic dampness (F#). Avoid placing the tuning fork directly on any skin lesion.

Capillaries: C#

In the present context, "capillaries" (*mai*) refer to the visible mesh of blood vessels that make the skin red. They are under the domain of the Fire phase and are controlled by C#. They can become dilated in hot conditions, resulting in localized swelling, redness, and warmth (see pathogenic heat above). They can also be affected by blood stasis, especially in the early period after trauma when there is redness, swelling and warmth at the injured site. Capillaries can also be involved in skin lesions where there is redness and swelling.

Flesh: F#

"Flesh" (*rou*) refers to the slippery, fatty tissues of the body as well as the soft bellies of large muscles. It is ruled by the Earth tone, F#. Flesh is often the site of chronic aches and soreness and is easily affected by damp. The flesh can also be affected by blood deficiency patterns, in which case there may be chronic diffuse aching or wasting of the tissues.

Sinew: A#

The term "sinew" (*jin*) has two meanings. On the one hand, it could refer to the hard and tendinous aspect of the muscle found near the joint, and this explains the common translation of this term as "tendon" in many texts. But it can also refer to the tone of the muscle as well as its ability to flex and extend smoothly. In either case, the sinews are controlled by Wood, the phase associated with resilience and smoothness, and they respond best to the Wood tone, A#. Disorders of the sinews might produce pain, restricted movement, tightness, spasms, tremors, and paralysis. Since the Wood organ, Liver, has the function of ensuring patency of qi and blood flow, the sinews are often the site of blood stasis. Symptoms might include bruising, soreness, and hard swellings, as might occur in the later stages after traumatic injury.

Bone: D#

Bone is the deepest of the five tissues and is associated with the Water tone, D#. Use this tone when the pain occurs directly in the joints, or is associated with deterioration of the bone mass and general health. D# should also be used for hard, palpable bone spurs, as may occur in chronic osteoarthritis.

Method 3: Select the Tone According to Depth of Symptoms

This method works best when treating points where there is considerable depth of tissue between the bone and the skin, as in the lower back and buttocks. It is also the method of choice for the acupuncturist that prefers to select his local points according to the presence of pressure pain or *kori*. The acupuncturist should assess the depth of tissue between the skin and bone at the chosen point, dividing it mentally into five layers according to Figure 2.19 below.

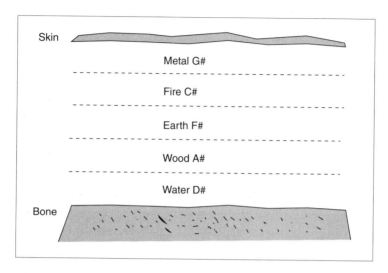

Figure 2.19 Layers of Tissue Between Skin And Bone

The correct tone to be employed is determined by the layer at which the symptoms are palpated. If, for example, the pain occurs when the point is pressed to the middle level—roughly in the belly of the belly of the muscle—the tone F# is used. If a *kori* is located in the area just below the skin level, the tone C# should be used. Note that these five levels tend to correspond roughly with the depth of the five tissues described in Method 2 above. The difference is that in the present technique, the determination of tone is made entirely by palpation rather than symptom analysis.

When the tuning fork is applied, the stem should be pressed to the appropriate level. In some cases, a single point or area might be the site of several levels of pain or *kori*. This is especially true in chronic conditions. In such cases, the practitioner should begin by dispersing the most superficial layer first, and then gradually work his way into the deeper levels. This might take several treatments.

Method #4: Select the Tone According to the Organ Being Treated

Use this method when you are using a point on the trunk to treat an organ, as in the cases of mu-alarm and shu-back points (for organ-tone associations, see Table 1.1). For example, if you are using UB 20 to treat the Spleen, use F#, the tone of Earth. If you are using UB 23 to treat the Kidney, use D#, the tone for Water. If, on the other hand, you are treating shu-back points simply because they are the sites of local muscle symptoms, it is probably better to select the tone according to methods 1-3 above, rather than according to the organ. Spasms and pain at UB 23, for example, are symptoms of the sinews, and should be treated with A#.

If you are using an intersection point such as CV 3, a determination must be made as to which organ or meridian you are wishing to access. If you are selecting CV 3 as a local point for the Urinary Bladder, then use D# (the tone for water). If you are using CV 3 as a local point for the uterus, then select the tone from one of the three meridians that connect with the uterus: Spleen, Liver, and Kidney. If you are treating menstrual pain due to Liver stagnation, for example, you might use A#; if you are treating menstrual pain due Spleen deficiency, you might use F#.

In all the above instances, you should supplement or drain according to the excess or deficiency status of the point selected. Painful swelling might be drained while dull intermittent aches might be supplemented. Use the supplementation and drainage techniques described in the previous section. You can also add some polish to the treatment by using one of the auxiliary methods described in Chapter 7.

8. Precautions and Contraindications

Acutone therapy performed with tuning forks alone is extremely safe. It would be prudent, however, to follow precautions similar to those involving acupuncture. During pregnancy, avoid stimulus of the abdomen and lower back, and avoid the points Sp 6, LI 4, UB 60, UB 67, Liv 3, and GB 21. Avoid direct contact of the tuning fork with sores, tumors, lesions or infected areas.

Neither of the authors has witnessed acupuncture syncope resulting from stimulus with tuning forks. Syncope is certainly possible if Acutone is combined with needle insertion, as described in Chapter 7. If signs of syncope occur, follow the conventional guidelines: withdraw all needles, lower the patient's head and use finger stimulus on GV 26.

Finally, it is important to remind the reader that Acutone, like other forms of natural healing, is not meant to be a substitute for conventional medical care. Acute illnesses and emergency conditions should be referred to physicians or trauma centers.

Chapter III

Review of Five-Phase Acupuncture

1. Five-Phase vs. Modern Chinese Treatment Styles

The five-phase Acutone root treatments presented in this book are designed for use in five-phase diagnostic and treatment models. If you are already practicing five-phase acupuncture, you can skip over this chapter and go straight to the five-phase Acutone treatments in Chapter 4. But if your training is based on modern Chinese methodology, the so-called "Eight-Parameter Acupuncture," you will need to become familiar with the five-phase system and how it is being used in modern Oriental therapy. What follows below is meant to be only a general introduction to the principles of five-phase treatment strategy, and space demands that we leave out many details. If the reader wishes to find a more comprehensive description of the five-phase system, we urge him to consult more definitive texts on this subject.[28]

In modern Chinese acupuncture, point selection is based on symptom patterns that are designed to dovetail with Chinese herbal therapy.[29] Selection of points for these patterns is based on modern convention, not historical rules. Although there are dozens of points that could theoretically be used to treat, for example, Spleen qi deficiency, most modern textbooks will recommend St 36, Sp 6, and UB 20, with other points added depending on the symptoms. Although we can try to explain these choices by saying that St 36 is the Great Point for the abdomen, or that Sp 6 is the Meeting Point of the three yin meridians of the leg; in truth these points are chosen because a consensus of modern Chinese clinicians consider them effective for the Spleen deficiency symptom complex. As a result, they form a kind of protocol that is used widely throughout China and tends to appear rather uniformly in modern Chinese texts.

This is not to say that modern Chinese acupuncture is fixed and rigid. Many senior acupuncturists create their own protocols, and new treatments are constantly being generated by research. But these newer treatments are usually predicated on their ability to directly impact the symptoms being addressed. It is often the case that the rationale for a treatment protocol is made after that protocol has been found to be effective, and this rationale is gathered as needed from whatever theories seem to best suit the circumstances.

It is unusual to find any *one* classical treatment paradigm being used consistently and in its entirety in modern Chinese textbooks. Classical tradition is consulted primarily for the wealth of empirical experience it contains, not for the value of its theories. Although there is a token acceptance of five-phase theory, for example, it is generally not used as a basis for selecting

[28] The authors recommend Shudo Denmei, *Introduction to Meridian Therapy*, transl. Stephen Brown, 1990, Eastland Press, Seattle.

[29] Ellis, Wiseman, and Boss, *Fundamentals of Chinese Acupuncture* , p.ii.

points unless those points coincide with conventional proto-cols. Taking the above example of Spleen deficiency, it would be rare to find a modern Chinese acupuncturist attempting to treat this pattern with Sp 2, even though this is the traditional supplementation point of the Spleen meridian.

Five-phase acupuncture differs in that the selection of treatment is built from fundamental theoretical principles and is governed by formal rules based on the interpretation of classical texts, most notably the *Nan Jing* (*Classic of Difficulties*, c. 1st centu-ry A.D.). The pulse plays a much more important role in estab-lishing the diagnosis, while disease symptoms are seen as only a secondary reflection of the deeper constitutional pattern reflected in the pulse. It is thought that disease, together with its symptoms, can only be rooted out by first addressing this constitutional pattern. In addition, there seems to be greater attention paid to the details of needling technique, especially in regard to the differentiation of supplementation and drainage.

The five-phase acupuncturist tends to have more faith in clas-sical theory, feeling that if he correctly follows the traditional treatment guidelines, the patient's condition cannot help but improve. Symptom-specific points are usually used only local-ly and are considered a minor aspect of the treatment. Since most constitutional problems are a result of deficiency, this means that there is a strong clinical emphasis on supplementa-tion. Perhaps most important of all, the five-phase diagnosis is not meant to be used as a basis for prescribing herbal therapy.

Since the pattern-confirmation methods of these two forms of acupuncture differ considerably, it is not surprising that they can yield entirely different diagnoses for the same patient. The same individual who is diagnosed in the modern Chinese sys-tem as Spleen qi deficient on the basis of having an empty pulse, pale tongue, loose stools and diffuse abdominal pain, could be diagnosed as *Liver* deficient in the five-phase system if the pulse is empty at the Liver and Kidney positions. Clearly, the two systems require different forms of diagnostic skill and insight, and the actual meaning of the diagnosis thus deciphered is different as well.

Although meridian stylists tend to look at their methods as being superior, it should be pointed out that treatment efficacy has more to do with the practitioner's skill than with the system being used, and virtually any style of acupuncture can be made to work effectively if the student is dedicated to mastering it. Your choice of treatment style should be based on your philosophy and intuition, not on any promise that one system is inherently "better." If you prefer to use the modern Chinese acupuncture methods, you will need to follow the twelve-meridian Acutone system presented later in this book. Nevertheless, we recommend trying both methods for some time before making a final decision.

2. The Generation and Restraining Cycle

As we have seen, the earliest ordering of the five-phases was the Cosmogonic Sequence, which was based on the pentatonic scale. But in the Han Dynasty, two new sequences became popular, and they later all but supplanted the earlier pentatonic system. These two sequences were called the *Xiang Sheng* or Generation Cycle and the *Xiang Ke* or Restraint Cycle. Beginning with Wood, the Generation Cycle follows the order:

Wood → Fire → Earth → Metal → Water → Wood

Wood burns to generate Fire; the ashes of Fire generate Earth; the Earth generates metal ore; Metal generates Water (like dew precipitating on a plow share); and Water is needed to grow trees to generate more Wood (Figure 3.1). In the Generation Cycle, each phase is referred to as the *mother* of the phase it generates, e.g., Wood is the mother of Fire, Fire is the mother of Earth, and so on. Likewise, the phase so generated is called the *child*, e.g., Fire is the child of Wood, Earth is the child of Fire and so on.

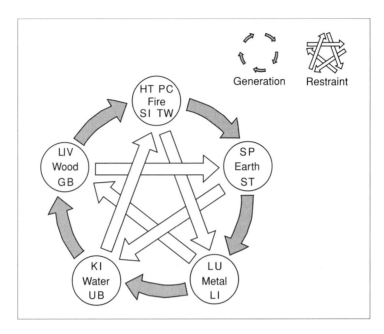

Figure 3.1 Generation/Restraint Cycle

As we pointed out earlier, the Generation Cycle symbolizes the growth of the created world. But this growth must be held in check by the Restraint Cycle, or it would gallop out of control. The Restraint Cycle follows the order:

Wood → Earth → Water → Fire → Metal → Wood

Wood restrains Earth (like grass roots that hold together sod), Earth restrains Water (by soaking it up), Water restrains Fire (by extinguishing it), Fire restrains Metal (by melting it), and Metal restrains Wood (like an ax felling a tree). The Restraint Cycle and Generation Cycle are actually integrated into one continuous sequence, as can be seen by studying Figure 3.1. If we move around the circle clockwise, we find that each phase generates the *next* phase in the clockwise sequence, but restrains the phase *after that*. For example, starting with Wood and moving clockwise, we find that it first generates Fire, but then restrains Earth.

In the same sense we can say that each phase is the *grand-mother*—the mother of the mother—of the phase it restrains. Thus, Wood is the grandmother of Earth, and Earth is the grandmother of Water. Likewise, each phase is the *grandchild* of the phase that restrains it, i.e., its child's child. For example, Earth is the grandchild of Wood, and Water is the grandchild of Earth. If the two cycles of Generation and Restraint are equally balanced, they should produce one happy extended family, and it is possible that the whole system was meant to represent a kind of ancestral lineage.

In the Han Dynasty, the five-phases became universal symbols that were systematically associated with all phenomena, including *zang*-organs, *fu*-bowels, seasons, planets, colors, tissues, and of course, musical tones. The most important phase ruler-ships for the present discussion are listed in Table 1.1. Based on the above principles, a series of rules are established that most five-phase acupuncturists agree with more or less.

Rule 1: Supplement the deficiency first

The primary cause of illness is deficiency of the yin organs, and therefore the fundamental goal of five-phase therapy is to identify the one yin organ whose deficiency is the root cause of the patient's sickness. In treatment, the practitioner always begins by supplementing this organ, and any draining is done later. Unlike other forms of acupuncture, where the diagnosis stems mainly from interview and symptom analysis, the five-phase diagnosis rests mainly on the pulse. In Japan, the pulse is usually confirmed by abdominal diagnosis and meridian palpation. The tongue is rarely employed.

Furthermore, organ deficiencies are not subdivided into yin deficiency, yang deficiency, blood deficiency, and qi deficiency, as they are in Chinese herbal medicine. That is because the diagnostic matrix of five-phase therapy stems from the proportionate strength of one organ vs. another, and not one substance vs. another.

Rule 2: Deficiencies tend to double up along the Generation cycle

As any parent knows, when a child becomes sick it will tend to drain energy from its mother. In like manner, the primary deficient meridian tends to create a deficiency in its mother organ, i.e., the organ that precedes it along the generation cycle. For example, if the Lung is deficient, it will cause a deficiency to occur in the Spleen. Although pulse diagnosis will reveal that the Lung and Spleen are both deficient, the *primary* deficiency is always considered to be in the child meridian—in this case the Lung—and therefore the pattern will be diagnosed as "Lung deficiency" (Figure 3.2). This leads to the next rule:

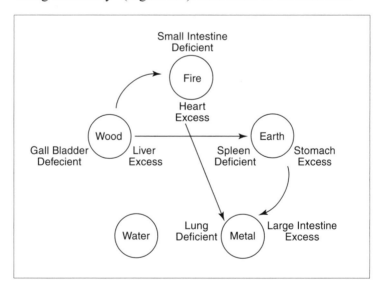

Figure 3.2 Lung Deficiency Pattern

Rule 3: Yin meridians (and their associated organs) tend toward deficiency and yang meridians (and their associated bowels) tend toward excess

Although yin meridians can experience a *reactive* excess (see Rule 5 below), a primary excess is considered quite rare. As a result, direct drainage of yin meridians tends to be avoided. By contrast, yang meridians are much more capable of experiencing excess due to their superficial location and their consequent tendency to absorb external pathogens. Thus, drainage techniques are far more likely to be used on yang meridians. Note that the Liver, often diagnosed as excess in modern Chinese practice, is much more likely to be called *deficient* in Japanese five-phase acupuncture. It is important, therefore, to stay within the rules of the system being practiced.

Rule 4: The Heart tends toward excess

The Heart is the one exception to Rule 3 above. Because of the Heart's critical position in sustaining life, it is believed by five-phase acupuncturists to possess a superabundance of energy. It is therefore the only yin organ whose usual pathological tendency is towards excess rather than deficiency. A *primary* deficiency in the Heart is believed to occur only in emergency conditions where Western intervention is needed. It is possible, however, for the Heart to have a *reactive* deficiency, as may occur in the Spleen deficiency pattern, where the Heart is deficient because it is the mother of the Spleen.

Many five-phase acupuncturists avoid treating the Heart meridian altogether, preferring to substitute the Pericardium meridian instead. Interestingly, there were no antique-*shu* points on the Heart meridian when the *Ling Shu* was written, and this may have reflected an important taboo in ancient Chinese society. The Heart represented the sovereign with whom one could never speak directly; grievances had to be addressed through his Minister, represented in the body by the Pericardium meridian. This is consistent with Acutone theory as well; recall that Sovereign Fire is the "toneless" phase, seemingly skipped over by the Cosmogonic Sequence (Figure 1.6).

Since primary deficiencies of the Heart are ruled out, we are left with just four deficiency patterns that form the basis of five-phase root treatment:

- Liver deficiency

- Kidney deficiency

- Spleen deficiency

- Lung deficiency

The vast majority of patients will fall into one of these four patterns. Although primary excesses in the yin meridians are theoretically possible, they are too rare to be covered in the present book. It is important to note that patients diagnosed with Heart deficiencies or Liver excesses according to modern Chinese methods would virtually always be reassigned to one of the above four patterns if they were reevaluated by a Japanese five-phase practitioner.

Rule 5: A deficient grandchild will tend to cause excess in its grandmother

Excesses and deficiencies tend to occur in a sea-saw manner along the Restraint Cycle. If the Lungs are deficient, for example, they tend to offer less resistance to the Heart's restraining power, and consequently, the Heart will tend to become excess (Figure 3.2). The excess so formed is not a true pathogenic excess but a *reactive* excess, an excess resulting entirely from the disproportionate distribution of the body's own energy. We might say that the Heart is becoming excess in order to *compensate* for the deficiency in the Lungs. It is important to realize that it is the deficiency of the grandchild organ that causes the reactive excess in its grandmother, and not vice versa.

Rule 6: When a yin meridian is deficient, its paired yang meridian tends to be excess, and vice versa

For example, when the Liver is deficient, the Gall Bladder tends to be excess, and when the Liver is (reactive) excess, the Gall Bladder tends to be deficient (Figure 3.2). This is another case of a sea-saw distribution of excess and deficiency. We might say that the Gall Bladder is compensating for the weakness in the Liver and vice versa. The rule is not hard and fast; there are many individual cases where yin-yang paired meridians both become deficient together; this is often the case with the Kidney and Urinary Bladder meridians.

Combining all the above rules, there are *eight* meridians that can theoretically be involved in a single pattern. In the case of the Lung deficiency pattern depicted in Figure 3.2, a deficient Lung will tend to drain energy from its mother organ, the Spleen. The deficiency in the Lung will also tend to cause reactive excess in its grandmother, the Heart, while the deficiency in the Spleen will tend to cause reactive excess in the Liver. We now have four yin organs involved in the Lung deficiency pattern: Lung and Spleen deficient, Liver and Heart excess. Finally, the yang meridians will become excess or deficient in a sea-saw pattern with their paired yin meridians. Thus the Lung deficiency will cause Large Intestine excess and the Spleen deficiency will cause Stomach excess; the Liver excess will cause Gall Bladder deficiency and the Heart excess will cause Small Intestine deficiency.

The above picture is somewhat theoretical; in real life it would be unusual for all eight meridians to fall perfectly into their expected excess-deficiency profiles. Of all the above tendencies, one can most reliably expect the primary yin meridian to be deficient together with its mother meridian (in the example above, this would be Lung and Spleen). In pulse diagnosis, therefore, *the practitioner should look for deficiencies in two yin meridians that are sequential on the Generation cycle*, i.e., a child and its mother. Let us be reminded once again that the tendency is for a deficient child to drain energy from its mother. The root pattern, therefore, will always be the *child* meridian in this mother-child pair.

For example, when the Spleen and Lung pulses are both deficient, the diagnosis will always be *Lung deficiency* (since the Lung is the child of the Spleen). When the Liver and Kidney pulses are both deficient, the diagnosis will always be *Liver deficiency* (since the Liver is the child of Kidneys).

3. Five-Phase Pulse Diagnosis

A five-phase root pattern is discerned primarily through the pulse. Since the goal of diagnosis is to establish the proportionate strength of different meridians, five-phase pulse diagnosis emphasizes pulse *position* rather than overall pulse quality. This is yet another distinction between five-phase and modern Chinese acupuncture styles.

The yin meridians are found on the deeper level of palpation at the three finger positions of the wrist (Figure 3.3), while the yang meridians are found at the superficial level. In order to accurately compare the various meridians, the pulses must be taken on both wrists simultaneously, and this is usually done with the patient lying supine and the practitioner standing on the patient's left side.

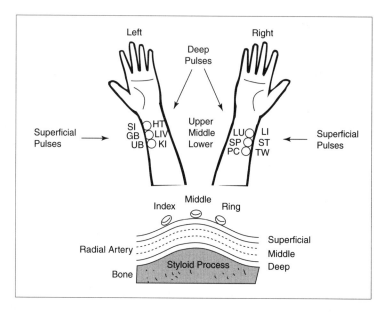

Figure 3.3 Pulse Positions and Qi Levels

The practitioner should begin by finding the styloid process of the wrists with his middle fingers, then moving slightly medial until the radial artery is felt. The index and ring fingers are then placed side-by-side next to the middle fingers. Next, the practitioner presses down until the pulse feels strongest and most easily discernible by all three fingers on both hands. This is called the *middle level*. In order to feel the pulse evenly on all finger positions, it is usually necessary to press somewhat more deeply with the index and ring fingers.

After finding the middle level, the practitioner should press a little more deeply, until the pulse is just barely able to slip underneath the fingers. This is the *deep level*. The deep level is the level of the *zang*-organs (fig 3.3); it is here that we look for the primary deficient meridian. As we stated above, one should look for deficiencies in two meridians that are related along the Generation Cycle. In the example of the Lung deficiency pattern just cited (Figure 3.2), there will be deficiencies at the

Lung and Spleen positions, i.e., at the index- and middle finger positions on the right pulse.

Once the primary deficiency has been identified, the finger pressure is released until the fingers are resting lightly above the artery and the pulse is just barely discernible. This is the *superficial level*. The superficial level is the level of the *fu*-bowels; it is here that we look for excesses and deficiencies of the yang meridians.

4. Five-Phase Treatment Guidelines

Once the root pattern has been diagnosed, one can commence the five-phase treatment. Recalling rule #1 above, *we always begin by supplementing the primary deficient meridian*. This will always be a yin meridian. Going back to the example depicted in Figure 3.2, the primary deficient meridian is the Lung and it is this meridian that we will supplement first.

After supplementing the primary meridian, we will then supplement its mother. In the example of Lung deficiency, the mother meridian is the Spleen. These two meridians, i.e, the primary deficient meridian and its mother, form the core of the five-phase root treatment. Let us examine the various rules involved in the point selection process.

Rule 1: When the child is deficient, supplement the mother

The implementation of this rule is divided into two steps. In the first step, *we must supplement the mother point of the primary meridian*. The "mother point," sometimes referred to as the "supplementation point," is the point that represents the mother phase of the meridian on which it is located. In the case of the Lung meridian, the mother point is the Earth point, Lu 9, since the Lung is ruled by Metal and the mother of Metal is Earth. In the case of Lung deficiency therefore, we would begin by supplementing Lu 9 (Table 3.1).

In the next step, *we must supplement the mother meridian.* In the case of the Lung deficiency of our present example, the mother meridian is the Spleen. Usually the mother meridian is supplemented by supplementing its *same-phase point*. The same-phase point, sometimes referred to as the "horary point," is the point that is controlled by the same phase as the meridian on which it is located. The same phase point of the Spleen meridian is its Earth point, Sp 3, since the Spleen is ruled by Earth.

The same-phase point is chosen when we are trying to avoid secondary effects on other meridians. If we were to supplement the Spleen meridian with its mother point, Sp 2 (the Fire point), it could cause a secondary supplementation of its mother *organ*, the Heart. This would be a mistake, since, as we learned earlier, the Heart tends be *excess*, especially in the Lung deficiency pattern.

After supplementing the primary meridian and its mother, one should reexamine the pulses. Sometimes these first two steps are all that is needed to bring about a satisfactory balance in the pulses and complete the root treatment. In most cases, however, excesses and deficiencies will remain in the other meridians involved in the pattern. The course of the rest of the root treatment will be determined by the response of the patient at each step. This brings us to the next rule of five-phase therapy:

Rule 2: Supplementation of the grandchild causes reduction of the grandmother and vice-versa

In effect, supplementation and reduction follow the sea-saw principle of the Restraining cycle that we encountered earlier. In the Lung deficiency pattern of Figure 3.2, the Heart and Liver meridians are originally in a state of reactive excess. Since the first two steps of the treatment supplemented their grandchildren, i.e., the Lung and Spleen, this may be all that was needed to eliminate the excess in the Heart and Liver.

If yin meridian excesses remain after the initial two steps, however, opinions differ on how to handle them. Some practitioners feel that yin meridians should never be drained *directly*, i.e., by points directly on the meridians themselves. These practitioners will skip to the next step below, and try to drain the yin meridians *indirectly* by supplementing their paired yang meridians.

If direct reduction of the yin meridians is to be attempted at all, it should be restricted to patients with strong constitutions and should always be performed with gentle techniques. If both grandmother meridians are excess, it is generally best to restrict treatment to the one which is strongest. Finally, since the Kidney meridian tends to be the most deficient meridian in the body, it should never be drained directly, even if it appears to be excess.

Usually, reduction of a grandmother yin meridian is accomplished by reducing its same-phase point. Let us assume, for example, that after the first two steps in treating the Lung deficiency of Figure 3.2, there remains an excess in the Heart meridian. This excess can be drained by reducing the same-phase point of the Heart meridian, Ht 8. As stated above, some practitioners prefer to avoid direct treatment of the Heart, in which case P 8, the same-phase point of the Pericardium, is drained instead.

After the excesses in the yin meridians have been taken care of, the practitioner should reexamine the pulses and look for excesses and deficiencies among the yang meridians. In most cases, only one or two yang meridians will need to be treated. To supplement or drain a yang meridian, one generally selects from one of three treatment points: the same-phase, yuan-source, or the luo-connecting points.

Let us assume, for example that after the steps described above, the Small Intestine meridian is found to be deficient. One could supplement SI 5, the same-phase (i.e. Fire) point of the Small Intestine. Alternatively, one could supplement SI 4 (yuan-source point) or SI 7 (luo-connecting point). This brings us to our third rule of treatment:

Rule 3: When treating yin-yang meridian pairs, supplementation of one meridian will cause reduction of its opposite and vice-versa

This rule is a practical consequence of the sea-saw principle involving yin-yang paired meridians encountered earlier. Using this principle, we can avoid direct reduction of a yin meridian. Instead, an excess yin meridian can be drained indirectly, by reducing its yang pair. Let us assume, for example, that in the case cited above we do not wish to drain the Heart meridian. We can drain it indirectly by supplementing the Small Intestine as we have already described. In order for this method to work, however, the Small Intestine meridian must not be excess.

After having supplemented the deficiencies in the yang meridians, one should look for excesses. Let us assume that after reexamination of the pulses in the above case, the Stomach meridian has been found to be excess. We choose to drain it by reducing St 40 (the luo-connecting point). Alternatively, we can drain the same-phase point (St 36) or the yuan-source point (St 42). We then reexamine the pulses one last time. If we are satisfied with the results, the five-phase root treatment is completed.

Let us summarize the steps involved in the imaginary treatment of the Lung-deficiency patient described above:

Step 1: Supplement the primary deficient meridian at its mother point, Lu 9

Step 2: Supplement the mother meridian at its same-phase point, Sp 3

- Reexamine pulses: Heart found to be excess; Small Intestine found to be deficient

Step 3: (optional) Drain the Heart at its same-phase point, Ht 8 (alternative: P 8)

Step 4: Supplement Small Intestine at its same-phase point, SI 5 (alternatives: SI 4, SI 7)

• Reexamine pulses: Stomach found to be excess

Step 5: Drain the Stomach at its luo point, St 40 (alternatives: St 42, St 36)

• Reexamine pulses: Treatment deemed satisfactory

Although the first two steps of the above treatment will apply almost universally to any patient with the Lung deficiency pattern, any subsequent steps will depend entirely on the response of the individual patient as discerned by reexamination of the pulse. For example, it is possible that, after completing Step 2, reexamination of the pulse indicated that the treatment had brought the other meridians into balance, in which case the need for any additional steps would have been eliminated. It is possible that, in checking the pulse after Step 2, the Liver was the meridian found to be most excess, and the Gall Bladder most deficient. It is also possible that excess could have occurred in the Large Intestine, and so on. In effect, the treatment could progress in several alternate directions depending on the response of the pulses at each step. In any case, regardless of which meridians are in need of treatment, the practitioner should follow the above point-selection principles.

Once the root treatment has been completed, five-phase practitioners will then direct their attention to local treatment. The local treatment involves the treatment of points on or near the symptomatic area. Examples might include LI 15 for the shoulder, or UB 52 for the lower back. In most cases, local treatment points are entirely empirical, and are selected according to pressure sensitivity or presence of *kori* (see Chapter 2). Since much of local treatment involves drainage, care must be taken not to undo the constitutional supplementation accomplished in the root treatment. If one has supplemented the Liver meridian, for example, it would be unwise to drain local points on that same meridian, as one might be inclined to do in case of medial knee pain.

5. Five-Phase Point Location Guidelines

Many five-phase acupuncturists, particularly those from Japan, believe that point location varies from patient to patient, and can even vary on the same patient from treatment to treatment. This is one more difference between the methodology of five-phase acupuncturists and that of modern Chinese practitioners, who tend to locate points according to stringent anatomical guidelines.

When locating root treatment points on yin meridians, the practitioner should lightly palpate the area of the selected point with the index finger of the left hand, feeling for the actual sensation of qi in the meridian. This is often described as a pulsation or vibration, although each practitioner will feel the sensation differently. The finger is then turned sideways to allow insertion of the needle, or in the case of Acutone, of the tuning fork.

When locating points on yang meridians, one is usually looking for a rough sensation on the skin that is analogous to the pulse-quality of the yang meridian being treated. If one is treating the Stomach, for example, and the Stomach pulse feels wiry, one should look for a "wiry" texture on the skin around St 40.

Palpation can also be used as a means of refining point selection. In the case of the wiry Stomach pulse just described, one can palpate St 40, St 42 and St 36 to see which has the texture that best matches the pulse. To a certain extent, one can also vary the selected treatment points of yin meridians, so long as the alternates do not violate any of the treatment principles outlined above. This means that if the requisite sensation cannot be found on the prescribed point, one can seek it at alternate treatment points. Some of the more common options for treatment of the four basic root patterns appear in Table 3.1.

	Main Treatment Points		Alternate Points	
Root Pattern	Child	Mother	Child	Mother
Liver Deficiency	Liv 8	Ki 10	Liv 1, Liv 3*	K 3*
Lung Deficiency	Lu 9	Sp 3	Lu 8	Sp 4, Sp 5
Kidney Deficiency	Ki 7	Lu 8	K 3*, K 10	Lu 5
Spleen Deficiency	Sp 3**	Ht 8, P 8	Sp 4	Ht 7, P7

Footnotes:

* Yuan-source points are sometimes prescribed independent of their five-phase properties.

** Sp 3 is likely to be substituted for Sp 2 by most practioners since supplementation of Sp 2 might cause accidental supplementation of the Heart meridian, which tends to be excess.

Table 3.1 Points For Supplementing Yin Meridians

As we stated at the outset of this chapter, our description of the five-phase treatment system is necessarily perfunctory. We have left out, for example, the use of Hara diagnosis and meridian palpation, which is used by most Japanese practitioners to confirm the pulse. A fuller presentation of Hara diagnosis as well as other elements of five-phase acupuncture can be found in Shudo Denmei's *Introduction to Meridian Therapy*.

Chapter IV

Five-Phase Acutone Treatment

1. Acutone Five-Phase Root Treatment

Having read the previous chapter, you now know how to diagnose a five-phase pathology and plan a five-phase treatment. We will next explain how to apply this treatment using Acutone therapy. To begin with, it is a good idea to plan the treatment in advance and mark the first few points with an eyebrow pencil or non-toxic marker. To locate the points used in Acutone root treatment, use the index finger of the non-treatment hand (if you are right handed this will be the left hand). Move the index finger *very* lightly in the vicinity of the point. As we mentioned earlier, most five-phase acupuncturists believe that the location of points are not rigidly fixed and vary from person to person and even within the same person from treatment to treatment. The correct location will be felt as a delicate pulsation, similar to the vibration of an artery but much finer.

Turn the tip of the index finger 90° while still keeping it on the skin. This exposes the point so that you can mark it. Still holding the index finger by the point, use it to guide the marker like a needle, and very lightly mark the point. If necessary, the mark can be removed later with water or alcohol. As you will soon see, some treatment points require the use of two tuning forks, one held in both hands. It is imperative that such points be marked in advance.

You may wish to familiarize yourself with the pentatonic notes that control each of the meridians according to Table 1.1. Note that the yang meridians are under the same phase-rulership as their yin pairs, and are therefore controlled by the same pentatonic note. For example, the Urinary Bladder and the Kidney are both ruled by D#. All the Fire meridians (i.e., Heart, Small Intestine, Pericardium, and Triple Warmer) are controlled by C#.

Now let us go through the entire five-phase root treatment, step by step. At some steps there are more than one options, and we will discuss these at the end of the chapter. We will be using the example of a patient with a Kidney deficiency pattern to describe the treatment process.

Step 1: Identify the primary yin meridian causing the pattern.

Example: Pulses indicate deficiency in the Lung and Kidney meridians, therefore the diagnosis is *Kidney deficiency* and the primary deficient meridian is *Kidney*.

Step 2: Referring to Table 1.1, select the tuning fork for the phase that rules the primary meridian. We shall refer to this as the *primary* fork. Then select the fork that corresponds to that meridian's mother, which we will call the *secondary fork*.

Example: The primary meridian in this treatment is the Kidney. The Kidneys are controlled by Water, so we select D#, the tone for Water. D# will be the primary fork. The mother of Water is Metal, and so we select G#, the tone for Metal. G# will be the secondary fork.

Step 3: Select the point that will best supplement the target meridian (see Table 3.1). This is usually the mother point.

Example: Kidneys are ruled by Water, and the mother of Water is Metal. So we will select the Metal point of the Kidney meridian, Ki 7.

Step 4: Locate and mark the point using the process described above.

Step 5: Hold the primary tuning fork in your right hand; hold the secondary tuning fork in your left hand (if you are left-handed reverse this). Strike both forks, then *slowly* advance the stem of the primary fork toward the point (we are using the supplementation technique described in Chapter 2). Once the stem of the primary fork has *lightly* contacted the skin, lower the stem of the secondary fork until it is slightly above the prongs of the primary fork. The two tuning forks will form a straight line (Figure 4.1). Be careful not to let the two forks touch.

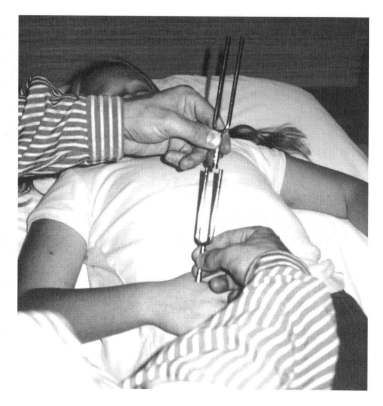

Figure 4.1 Simultaneous Use of Primary and Secondary Forks on a Single Point (LI 4)

Example: To supplement Ki 7, hold the **D#**-fork in the right hand, the **G#**-fork in the left. Strike both forks. Lower the stem of **D#** slowly until it lightly contacts the skin at Ki 7 (be careful not to press too hard). Then lower **G#** until its stem is slightly above the prongs of **D#**, the two forks forming a straight line.

Step 6: Hold both forks steady until the tone of the primary fork has almost completely died out. Now withdraw the secondary fork and palm it in your left hand or tuck it in you pocket. Then *swiftly* withdraw the primary tuning fork while simultaneously "closing" the exposed point with the index finger of the left hand (Figure 4.2). This will take some practice.

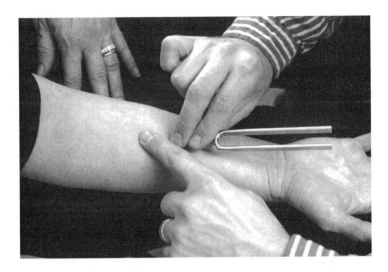

Figure 4.2 Withdrawing Fork and Closing Hole (The Point Being Treated is P 4)

Example: Once D# has stopped vibrating on Ki 7, withdraw **G#** and palm or pocket it. Then place your left index finger on the edge of the stem of the **D#**-fork. Withdraw D# swiftly while gently pressing down on Ki 7 with the left index finger.

Step 7: Recheck the pulse and repeat if necessary. It is possible to repeat this technique up to three times.

Step 8: Go to the mother meridian and select an appropriate point. This is usually the same-phase point. Locate and mark the point as above.

Example: The primary meridian is Kidney; the mother of Kidney (Water) is Lung (Metal). So locate and mark the Metal point (i.e., the same-phase point) of the Lung meridian, Lu 8.

Step 9: Repeat the supplementation procedure on the mother meridian, but this time use only *one* tuning fork—the fork that represents the phase of the mother meridian (this is the same fork that was the secondary fork used in Step 2). Strike this tuning fork and use the left hand, which is now free, to relocate the point. Now turn the left index finger 90° and hold it over the point while the right hand advances the stem of the fork. When the stem reaches the point, use the left index finger to help support it around the point. Use supplementation technique as above for insertion and withdrawal.

Example: The Lung meridian is ruled by Metal, so select the G# tuning fork. Strike the fork and relocate Lu 8 with the left index finger. Turn the index finger 90° while holding it on the point, being careful not to press too hard. With the right hand, slowly lower the stem of the G#-fork until it lightly contacts the skin at Lu 8. When the vibration has nearly died out, withdraw the fork quickly with the right hand while pressing gently on the point with the index finger of the left hand.

Step 10: Recheck the pulses. If there are excesses or deficiencies in the yang meridians, treat them with supplementation or drainage technique, using the tone for the phase that controls each meridian. As described in Chapter 3, the best points for treating yang channels in five-phase root treatment are the same-phase, yuan-source, or luo-connecting points.

Example: After supplementing Ki 7 and Lu 8 on our Kidney deficient patient, pulses indicate excess in the Urinary Bladder and deficiency in the Small Intestine. To supplement the Small Intestine, we select SI 4, the yuan-source point. Since the Small Intestine is ruled by Fire, we will supplement it with **C#**. We will use only one tuning fork, repeating the one-fork supplementation technique just described.

Next we drain the Urinary Bladder meridian with UB 64, the yuan-source point. Since the Urinary Bladder is ruled by Water, we will use **D#**. Once again, we will use only one tuning fork, but this time we will *drain*. We strike the tuning fork hard, relocate UB 64 with the left index finger, and push the stem to the skin *rapidly*. When contact is made with the skin, we should press a little bit harder, but not too hard. While the fork is still vibrating, slowly withdraw it, letting go with the left hand and leaving the hole open.

Step 11 (Optional): To fortify the root treatment you may want to supplement the Shu-back or Mu-Alarm points that correspond with the primary organ and its mother. Use supplementation technique with a single fork on each point. Match the fork to the phase of the organ ruled by each point.

Example: In our Kidney-deficient patient, we will supplement the shu-back points of the Kidney, UB 23, with D#, and the Shu-back points of the Lungs, UB 13 with G#.

It is important to note that in the above treatment, two tuning forks are used simultaneously in the initial treatment of the primary meridian. *All the other points that follow must be treated with a single tuning fork.* Why is this?

Dean Lloyd arrived at this technique through trial and error, after failing to get the appropriate response by using only the tone of the meridian. In fact, if single tones are used in the primary meridian, our experience has shown that the treatment may have the *opposite* effect, i.e., it may drain instead of supplement. Dean has reasoned that the primary tone must be given *direction* by another tone in order to impel the treatment toward the intended supplementation or drainage. If only one tone is used on the primary meridian, the body is not likely to recognize it as having any specific biological impetus. In order for that first tone to have meaning, it must be established as having a place in a *scale*, and this requires that one other tone be struck simultaneously.

Once the treatment scale has been communicated to the body's energy, we do not want to confuse it by playing too many notes. Therefore, only one fork is used at a time in the subsequent steps of the treatment.

2. Variations in Five-Phase Root Treatment

There are actually several different ways in which the two initial tones can be introduced into the primary meridian. Instead of holding two forks above a single point, it is possible to select *two points* on the primary meridian. The primary tuning fork should be placed on the point which is most crucial to the treatment, and the secondary fork should be placed on the supporting point (Figure 4.3).

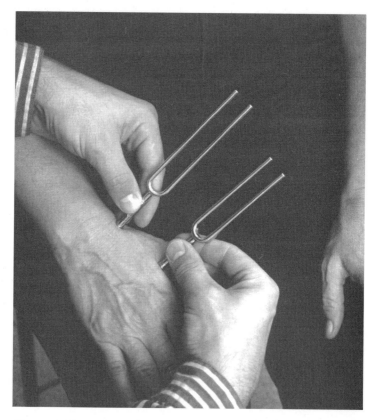

Figure 4.3 Treating the Large Intestine Meridian with LI 4 and LI 5

Example: In the Kidney-deficient patient we have been treating, we might elect to place **D#** on Ki 10, the Water point, and **G#** on Ki 7, the metal point. This way we are treating two sequential points on the Generation cycle, and we are matching the tuning fork frequencies to the phase energies of each selected point. Of course there are many other combinations of points, and it is up to the practitioner to make the selection based on the various guidelines introduced in Chapter 3.

When you treat two points simultaneously in this fashion, hold one fork in each hand as before. This time, hold each fork in the hand that is closest to the point it is going to treat. Apply the primary fork to the primary treatment point *first*, and the secondary fork to the supporting point *second*. Withdraw the forks in the reverse order. The supplementation technique will be the same as above, except that you will only need to close the hole on the primary treatment point.

Example: To supplement the Kidney meridian, hold the D#- and G#-forks in each hand as before. Strike both forks and begin by slowly lowering the stem of D# to Ki 10. As soon as it contacts the skin, hold it in place while lowering G# to Ki 7 with the opposite hand. Hold both forks motionless on the two points. When the vibration of D# has almost died out at Ki 10, continue to hold it in place while quickly withdrawing G# from Ki 7. Palm or pocket the G#-fork, then use the index finger of the free hand to close the hole on Ki 10 while rapidly withdrawing the D#-fork. Since you only have two hands, you will only be able to close the hole of the main treatment point.

Some practitioners might decide to look for excesses in the grandmother meridians after step 9. As we explained in Chapter 3, drainage of yin meridians is a risky business, even when they are in a state of excess. Thus, any such procedure must be done gently and carefully.

Step 9a: Identify which of the two grandmother yin meridians is the most excess, and select an appropriate treatment point on it; this will usually be the same-phase point.

Example: In our Kidney-deficient patient, we check the pulse after supplementing the Kidney and Lung meridians. It reveals excess in the Heart meridian. Following the taboo against treating the Heart directly, we select the same-phase point of the Pericardium meridian, P 8.

Step 9b: Using the tuning fork that matches the phase of the chosen meridian, drain the selected point using the single-fork drainage technique described above.

Example: The Pericardium is ruled by Fire, so we use the **C#** tuning fork. Locate P 8 with the left hand and strike the fork loudly with the right hand. Lower the fork swiftly toward the point. When contact is made with the skin, press the stem of the fork a little bit harder, but not too hard. While the fork is still vibrating, slowly withdraw it, letting go with the left hand and leaving the hole open.

There are, in fact, many different methods for performing five-phase root treatment. Almost any five-phase point selection methodology can be adapted to Acutone, so long as the treatment begins with two tones applied simultaneously to the primary meridian. We recommend that you keep the treatments as simple as possible in the beginning, focusing on proper diagnosis and stimulation technique.

3. Local Treatment in Five-Phase Acutone

In some cases, root treatment is all that is needed to resolve the problem. Most of the time, however, there will be some local treatment points added after the root treatment, especially if the main complaint is local pain. In five-phase Acutone, local treatment is almost always done after the root treatment is complete and the pulses show sufficient balance. Administer the local treatment according to the principles described in Chapter 2, using only one fork at a time on each point.

Many five-phase practitioners prefer to select their local points according to palpation for pressure-pain or *kori* (see Chapter 2). Almost any point on the surface of the body might show such findings, and so it is not necessary to restrict treatment to anatomically located textbook points. After a five-phase root treatment, however, it is best to keep the local treatment conservative, with gentle stimulus on as few points as possible.

The biggest mistake that can be made at this stage is over-treatment. One should avoid treating any points that might undo the supplementation that was so painstakingly accomplished in the root treatment. In general, points located on the head, neck, and trunk are the best for local treatment, since their effects tend to be restricted to these local areas. Points on the extremities, however—especially those distal to the knees and elbows—tend to affect the circulation of the entire meridian. In five-phase Acutone we try to reserve these points for root treatment only.

Example: If our Kidney deficient patient complains of pain in the shoulder along the Small Intestine meridian, you can safely disperse the local points on the shoulder so long as you proceed gently (you will find a detailed description of such a treatment in Chapter 6). It would be unwise, however, to drain the Small Intestine meridian using distant points (such as SI 3 or SI 6), since we just finished supplementing this meridian in the main treatment.

If the same patient complains of pain in the medial knee, it would be unwise to drain local points around K 10, since this would jeopardize the Kidney supplementation just achieved. There are several different ways to approach such a problem. It is possible to simply leave the knee alone, allowing the root treatment itself to produce the desired result. Alternatively, the local points on the knee can be *supplemented*, since they are likely to be deficient anyway. Yet another method is to select the most excess yang meridian in the affected area, and drain a few local points on it. Recall that in the present example, the Urinary Bladder meridian was excess. So we might drain local points such as UB 39 or UB 40. In either case, be sure to double-check the pulses after administering such a treatment. If they have changed, you will have to re-supplement the Kidney meridian.

Chapter V

The Creation of the Twelve-Meridian Scale

1. The Twelve Pitch-Pipes

The treatment paradigm we have been studying up until now has revolved entirely around the five-phases. The treatment options presented by this paradigm are of necessity limited by the fundamental laws that govern the ways in which the five-phases interact. In effect, there are only two possible relationships that can occur between any two phases: Generation and Restraint. But the body has a total of *twelve* main meridians, all of them having an important role in the treatment of illness. If we step outside the pure five-phase paradigm, as many modern acupuncturists prefer to do, we not only find a far greater number of meridian relationships, but we also gain permission to treat those meridians in ways that ignore the consequences of the Generation and Restraint cycles. In so doing we widen our treatment choices and attain a system that dovetails with modern Chinese reference works such as Cheng Xinnong's *Chinese Acupuncture and Moxabustion*. This is the style of acupuncture we referred to in Chapter 3 as "Eight Parameter" or "modern Chinese." For reasons that will soon become apparent, we will now refer to it as "twelve-meridian acupuncture," or, in the present context, *twelve-meridian Acutone*.

As it so happens, the pentatonic scale upon which the five-phase system is built has its own limitations as well, and this was long ago recognized by Chinese musicians. Consequently, a larger duodecatonic (twelve-note) scale, similar to our Western chromatic scale, was developed as early as the 6th century B.C. Its principle function in Zhou Dynasty music was to allow the pentatonic scale to be played in twelve different keys. Considering that there are five possible modes in a pentatonic scale, this allows for a total of sixty possible mode-keys[30]; one, potentially, for each of the sixty stem-branch combinations of Chinese astrology.

An examination of the role these various mode-keys might play in Acutone therapy will have to be saved for future works by the authors. For the sake of the present discussion, it is the function of the Chinese chromatic scale as a reference-point for absolute frequency that concerns us. We have already learned that the Han Dynasty fundamental was set by the eighty-one *fen* pitch-pipe called *Huang Zhong*. Using the *san fen sun yi* method of increasing and decreasing consecutive pipe-lengths described in Chapter 1, the *Huang Zhong* was used to create a gamut of twelve pitch-pipes (*shi er lu*) that established the frequencies for the Chinese chromatic scale (see Appendix B). The names of the twelve pitch pipes are presented in Table 5.1 as they appear in *Lu Shi Chun Qiu* (*Master Lu's Springs and Autumns Annals* c. 3rd century B.C.)[31]. The name of the pipe was also the name of the note it represented in the scale[32].

---

[30] Chen Cheng-Yih, 1996, p. 45-46.

[31] Chen Cheng-Yih, 1994, p. 169-171.

[32] The names of the twelve pitch-pipes are not consistent in the various classical texts nor in the inscriptions on Chinese bells (see Von Falkenhausen 287).

Pitch-Pipe	Possible Translation	Modern Equivalent
Yin Zhong	Answering bell	E
Wu Yi	Not terminated	D#
Nan Lu	Southern Lu (a surname = pipe?)	D
Yi Ze	Equalizing standard	C#
Lin Zhong	Forest bell	C
Rui Bin	Luxuriant vegitation	B
Zhong Lu	Intermediate Lu (a surname = pipe?)	A#
Gu Xian	Related to Xian (a surname = purity?)	A
Jia Zhong	"In-between" bell	G#
Tai Cu	Greater frame (? for silkworm cacoons)	G
Da Lu	Great Lu (a surname = pipe?)	F#
Huang Zhong	Yellow bell	F

Table 5.1 Pitch-Pipe Translations

While the *Ling Shu (Mystical Pivot)* correlated ten of the twelve meridians with the notes of the pentatonic scale,[33] we have thus far found no record of any attempt by the Chinese to match all twelve meridians with the twelve pitch pipes. To the best of our knowledge, the first attempt to link frequencies in such a manner appears in the work of Fabien Maman, the modern musician, composer and acupuncturist. In his words, "The mathematical correspondence between these two systems was too tempting not to try to work with them."[34] Maman published the conclusions of his research in 1997 in *Sound and Acupuncture: The Body As Harp*. His system of meridian-tone correspondence is listed in Table 5.2.

---

[33] *Ling Shu (Mystical Pivot*, Liansheng Wu, Nelson and Andrew Qi Wu, transl.), ch. 64-65. It is noteworthy that no tones were assigned in the Ling Shu to the Triple Warmer or Pericardium meridians.
[34] Maman, 1997c, p. 73.

Chromatic Scale	Twelve Meridians
E	Tripple warmer
D#	Pericardium
D	Kidney
C#	Urinary bladder
C	Small Intestine
B	Heart
A#	Spleen
A	Stomach
G#	Large intestine
G	Lung
F#	Liver
F	Gall bladder

Table 5.2 Correlation Between the Chromatic Scale and the Twelve Meridians

Maman advances the idea that the twelve-meridian scale begins at the Gall Bladder meridian with F-natural as a fundamental. Our own research and experience has since verified the validity of this choice. Two questions immediately present themselves: why begin the scale at the Gall Bladder meridian, and why is F-natural the fundamental?

Let us begin by considering the first of these questions. Most modern acupuncturists are aware of the correlation between the twelve meridians and the twelve hours of the Chinese clock (Figure 5.1). But the twelve-hour clock is itself only one aspect of a more comprehensive duodecimal sequence that links together all twelve-fold cyclical phenomena in Chinese cosmology, including hours, months, years, meridians, and of course, pitch-pipes. The coordinates of this sequence are called the Twelve Earthly Branches (*Shi Er Di Zhi*) and the wheel they engender is referred to as the *Zi-Wu* cycle, after the respective first and seventh branches in the sequence. To provide an easier frame of reference we will refer to the Twelve Branches by their numerical equivalents (Table 5.3).

Zi	Chou	Yin	Mao	Chen	Si	Wu	Wei	Shen	You	Xu	Hai
I	II	III	IV	V	VI	VII	VIII	IX	X	XI	XII

Table 5.3 Numerical Equivalents of the Twelve Earthly Branches

Referring to Figure 5.1, we can see that Branch I matches up with the Gall Bladder meridian and with the "midnight" hour of the Chinese clock.[35] Thus, the true beginning of the meridian circulation is in the Gall Bladder, just as the true beginning of the day is at midnight. The Lung meridian occurs further up the cycle, at Branch III.

---

[35] Actually the first hour is 11:00 P.M to 1:00 A.M.; this means that the Chinese day begins at 11:00 PM the previous day.

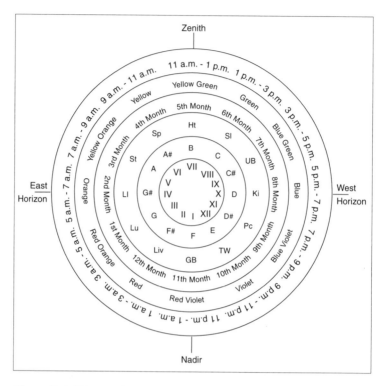

Figure 5.1 Chinese Clock

Why then do most Chinese textbooks, including the *Ling Shu* itself [36], assume that the meridian circulation begins in the Lung? This apparent discrepancy is best explained by correlating the Lung meridian with the Chinese cycle of months. As shown in Figure 5.1, Branch III coincides with both the Lung meridian and the first month of the Chinese year. The first day of this month is the familiar Chinese New Year, occurring midwinter by Western reckoning. The true astronomical reference point for the Chinese New Year, however, is the winter solstice at Branch I, even though this is the eleventh month in the Chinese calendar.[37]

---

[36] *Ling Shu (Mystical Pivot*, Liansheng Wu, Nelson and Andrew Qi Wu, transl.), ch. 10.
[37] Walters p.55.

As we learned in Chapter 2, the winter solstice represents the hidden beginnings of the year—the "antinode" where the sun reverses direction and begins its northern ascent. While the yang energy is "conceived" at Branch I, it is not made manifest in the world until it reaches Branch III, when the weather begins to warm. By the same token, the daily cycle of the sun's new energy—represented by the growth of yang qi in the meridians—has its hidden beginning deep in the Gall Bladder meridian at midnight, and does not become visible until it reaches the Lung meridian at dawn. As one of the present authors described in *Practical Application of Meridian Style Acupuncture*,[38] the coincidence of the Gall Bladder meridian with the sun's nadir explains its function as the body's yang "pivot."

In the *Huai Nan Zi* (*Lord of Huai Nan*, 2nd cent. B.C.), the twelve pitch pipes were matched with the twelve months.[39] The *Huang Zhong* was associated with the eleventh month, which in turn corresponds with Branch I and the Gall Bladder meridian. When all these correspondences have been collected together, it becomes self-evident that the Chinese chromatic scale must begin with its lowest frequency at the Gall Bladder meridian.

But why is this frequency F? To explain this we must return to the generation of the pentatonic scale through perfect fifths (see Chapter 1). As you recall, the scale sequence began with F#, and moved up by fifths to successively generate C#, G#, D#, and finally A#. Each note in the scale had reached upward to find its perfect fifth—the one tone with which it would resonate most harmoniously—except for the unfortunate A#, which was left alone without a musical soul-mate. The perfect fifth that A# is seeking is none other than F, a tone which is not within the reach of the pentatonic scale.

---

[38] Pirog, *Practical Application of Meridian-Style Acupuncture*, 1996, p. 60.

[39] See Fung Yu-lan 1934, p. 13-15.

This sense of incompleteness is dramatically illustrated in Figure 1.6, where the lines of pentatonic fifths form a near-perfect pentagram. Note that the pentagram points down to Wood/A#, the final phase-note as we are climbing up the cycle of fifths from *Gong* F#. The dotted line shows the direction in which the A# must move in order to find its upper fifth. By transferring A# to the Spleen meridian and arranging the other frequencies of the chromatic scale in the twelve meridians around it, we find that F falls right into the Gall Bladder meridian—the Wood phase which was previously occupied by A#. Fabien Maman refers to this exchange of positions as the "inversion between the Wood and the Earth."

In other words, in order for A# to find its perfect fifth, it must transcend the five-phases and give birth to a new frequency that is outside the range of the pentatonic scale. This new frequency is F, which becomes the starting point for an entirely new species of scale, one in which a whole new progression of notes and half-notes are formed, each linked with its own perfect fifth. If we once again draw lines through the *Zi Wu* chart to connect these fifths, we have a perfect twelve-pointed star (Figure 5.2).

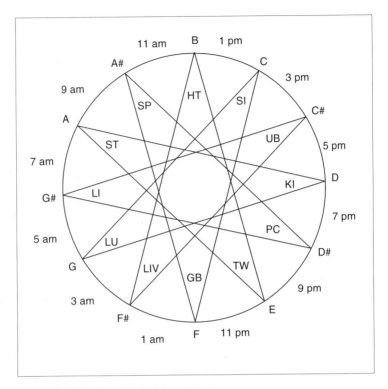

Figure 5.2 Twelve Pointed Star/Zi Wu

In short, the pentatonic scale telescopes into the chromatic scale as part of a single evolutionary process. The twelve notes of the chromatic scale, together with the meridians they control, allow the pentatonic scale to become part of a higher ordering of the universe. In this higher order, the meridian circulation becomes a self-contained, self-perpetuating wheel of musical motion, connecting in one complete circle the energies of the head, chest, hands and feet.

Because the two scales give birth to different circulation paradigms, they must of necessity control the meridians with *different notes*. In the pentatonic scale, for example, the Gall Bladder is ruled by A#, the pentatonic note for the Wood phase. In the chromatic scale, however, the Gall Bladder is ruled by F. *The note we use, and the way in which we use it, will depend on whether we are using five-phase or twelve-meridian Acutone systems.* It is important, therefore that the two systems are not confused.

2. The Twelve-Meridian Color-Wheel

While our discussion thus far has centered on the primacy of F as a fundamental note, the Acutone therapeutic system is equally concerned with F as a fundamental *frequency*. As explained in Chapter 1, estimates of the *Huang Zhong* frequency have ranged from F to G# (see Appendix A). While the Acutone system might be able to accommodate some limited variability in this area, we believe the correct frequency falls closest to F.

It is important to understand that all vibrating systems can be defined by frequency. Just as frequency determines the pitch of a tuning fork or flute, so also it determines the color of the visible spectrum. In the Taoist conception of the universe, light and sound are two aspects of a single continuum of energy, separated only by their frequencies. If we raise the frequencies of our chromatic scale by forty octaves, we will have moved from the realm of sound to the realm of light.

The very term *chromatic scale* (literally, "colored scale") suggests that musicians have long had an intuitive recognition of the link between color and pitch. Thus, it should come as no surprise to the modern Taoist that the visible spectrum of light encompasses approximately *one octave*. In effect, the color wheel is a kind of scale. We can take any note in the musical scale, therefore, and "transform" it into a color in the visible spectrum by simply raising the frequency forty octaves. *All visible colors can be seen as higher octaves of musical tones.*

Let us take, for example, the frequency of a modern C_5 in the Just scale, which starts at 512.0 Hz. If we raise this Figure forty octaves we will have 562.9 *trillion* Hz, the frequency of the color *green*. In Table 5.4 we have arranged the frequencies of the color spectrum together with their lower-octave equivalents in the chromatic scale. The frequency calculations are based on a Just scale set to C_4 at 256.0 Hz.

Table 5.4 clearly demonstrates that the spectrum of visible light begins and ends at the higher-octave equivalents of the note F. The visible spectrum begins at red-violet (375.7 trillion Hz), 40 octaves above F_4, and ends at violet red (751.4 trillion Hz), 40 octaves above F_5. Even if the upper and lower limits of the visible spectrum are reduced, as they are in some individuals, the higher octave equivalents of the F-note will still occur at the approximate transition points between visible and invisible light. The color "scale" thus begins and ends at F, and this clearly establishes F as the fundamental frequency *par excellence*, the starting and ending note of both the scale of sound and the scale of light, the true *Huang Zhong*.

Note	Frequency (Hz)	Frequency X 40 Octaves (in Trillion Hz)	Color	
B5	966.5	1063	Ultraviolet spectrum	
A#5	912.3	1003		
A5	861.1	946.8		
G#5	812.8	893.6		
G5	767.1	843.5		
F#5	724.1	796.1		
F5	683.4	751.4	Violet red	Visible spectrum
E5	645.1	709.3	Violet	
D#5	608.9	669.5	Blue violet	
D5	574.7	631.9	Blue	
C#5	542.4	596.4	Blue green	
C5	512.0	562.9	Green	
B4	483.3	53.14	Yellow green	
A#4	456.1	501.5	Yellow	
A4	430.5	473.4	Yellow orange	
G#4	406.4	446.8	Orange	
G4	383.6	421.7	Red orange	
F#4	362.0	398.1	Red	
F4	341.7	375.7	Red violet	
E4	322.5	354.6	Infrared spectrum	
D#4	304.4	334.7		
D4	287.4	315.9		
C#4	271.2	298.2		
C4	256.0	281.5		

Table 5.4 Octavic Conversion From Sound to Light Frequencies

Chapter VI

Twelve-Meridian Acutone Treatment

1. Principles of Supplementation and Drainage

Those practitioners who wish to incorporate Acutone into a modern Chinese treatment paradigm will need to employ the twelve-meridian techniques described below. This method of Acutone correlates more closely with "Eight-Parameter" styles of acupuncture and with modern Chinese manipulative therapy (*tui na*). As we explained in Chapter 3, modern Chinese practice tends to place empirical experience above strict classical rules, and so the diagnosis and treatment can be pieced together with greater flexibility than when choices are governed entirely by the laws of the five-phases. Twelve-meridian Acutone can therefore be made to follow the treatment strategies contained in modern Chinese textbooks such as Chen Xinnong's *Chinese Acupuncture and Moxabustion*.

In this style of therapy, it is not always necessary to begin with a root treatment of the internal organs, and there is less overall emphasis on supplementation. In case of uncomplicated external problems such as local pain, the treatment can be built on simple local-distant point combinations. For example, a patient with shoulder pain along the Small Intestine meridian can be treated with local and distant points on this meridian alone. Nevertheless, twelve-meridian Acutone is a meridian-based system formed on classical circulation models, and in order to adapt it to modern Chinese treatment strategies, specific meridians *must* be targeted in order to make use of the chromatic scale. Furthermore, the meridian-tone selection process necessitates that we make a choice between supplementation and drainage in each meridian we treat.

Because the pentatonic and chromatic scales give birth to different circulation paradigms, they must of necessity control the meridians with *different notes*. In the pentatonic scale, for example, the Gall Bladder is ruled by A#, the pentatonic note for the Wood phase. In the chromatic scale, however, the Gall Bladder is ruled by F. Furthermore, unlike the five-phase system, the chromatic scale assigns each of the twelve meridians its own unique note. *The note we use and the way in which we use it will depend on whether we are using five-phase or twelve-meridian Acutone systems.* It is critical, therefore, that these two systems are not confused.

Always observe the following rule:

- When performing *five-phase* Acutone, use the pentatonic tone-meridian correspondences from Table 1.1.

- When performing *twelve-meridian* Acutone, use the chromatic tone-meridian correspondences from Table 5.2.

It is important to understand that the pentatonic and chromatic scales access the meridian energies in different ways, and each utilizes a different principle to effect supplementation or drainage. When performing five-phase Acutone, for example, the true target of treatment is the internal organs, and so we must access each meridian in a way that sends the therapeutic stimulus most directly to this target. In other words, the meridian serves merely as a conduit that links inner organ with outer world—microcosm with macrocosm. The connection between these two worlds can be made most directly through the one group of symbols they both share in common: the five-phases. To directly access the organs, therefore, we use the pentatonic notes of the five-phases. If we are supplementing the Gall Bladder meridian with A#, for example—the pentatonic tone for Wood—we are bringing some of the cosmic Wood energy— the regenerative forces of spring—into the Gall Bladder organ itself.

If we are only using the Gall Bladder meridian to treat an external problem like sciatica, however, its therapeutic role is very different. In this case it is unnecessary—and perhaps inappropriate—to interfere with the energies of the Gall Bladder *organ*, since the real goal of therapy is to restore circulation to the Gall Bladder *meridian*. It is the function of the meridian as a pathway of circulation from body-part to body-part that we wish to access, and so we must approach the Gall Bladder meridian with its note from the chromatic scale, F.

While it is true that the two systems of Acutone affect the meridians in different ways, they can both be used to treat the same types of conditions. While the five-phase system, for example, is based on treatment of the internal organs, we learned in Chapter 4 that it can definitely be used to treat external disorders, so long as the treatment begins with root supplementation of the organs and the local treatment is carefully limited. Likewise, as we are about to see, the twelve-meridian system can be used to treat *internal* disorders. The results will be obtained through different principles, however. When we supplement an organ with the five-phase system we are harmonizing it with the seasons and—by extension—with the other organs in the body through the rules of the Generation and Restraint cycles. When we are supplementing an organ in the twelve-meridian system, however, we are regenerating it with energy taken from the body itself, drawn from meridian-to-meridian through the circulation of the Zi-Wu cycle. *Although each system can be used to treat the same problem, therefore, each will have its own unique treatment principles, and the student must be careful not to mix systems.*

Because different musical laws govern twelve-meridian Acutone, *there are different rules for supplementation and drainage.* It is imperative, therefore, that we follow the rules of tone selection that apply to the species of scale being employed. In the five-phase Acutone treatment described in Chapter 4, we needed to apply two tones simultaneously to the primary meridian in order to direct the treatment toward supplementation or drainage, and any subsequent meridian was treated with only a single tone. But in twelve-meridian Acutone, *we will use two tones for every meridian being treated.* Single tuning forks are only used when zeroing in on local points. This bears some explanation.

We have already learned the chromatic notes associated with each of twelve meridians (Figure 5.1). Notice that the difference between one meridian and another in the chromatic sequence is only a half step. In order to make any specific meridian stand out as a therapeutic target, therefore, a second note needs to be added to the fundamental. Furthermore, this second note must make a *musical statement* regarding the target meridian: it must either supplement or drain.

In twelve-meridian Acutone, therefore, the rules for supplementation and drainage are based entirely on music theory. Here is how they work:

- To supplement, use the fundamental (primary fork) together with the perfect fifth *below* it.

• To drain, use the fundamental (primary fork) together with the major third *above* it.

Suppose we want to supplement the Small Intestine meridian. Referring to Table 6.1 below, we see that the fundamental for the Small Intestine is C. Thus the C-fork is the primary fork used to treat this meridian. The perfect fifth below C is F; so we will use the primary C-fork together with the F-fork. If we want to reduce the Small Intestine, we will use the C-fork together with the E-fork, the major third above C. When placed side- by-side in the same octave, the notes E and F are only a half-note apart; the same holds for all lower fifth / upper major third combinations. This interval does not occur by chance. Since the meridian scale is itself built on half-note increments, the difference between supplementing and draining cannot be more than the increments in the scale.

From a musician's perspective, the rule makes perfect intuitive sense. The rousing intensity of *Reveille* is caused by perfect fifths, while the calming softness of *Brahm's Lullaby* is the result of a melody based on major thirds. In acupuncture, supplementation is defined as an augmentation or "raising" of the energy; this is clearly analogous to the raising of a note through the rules of musical harmony. To supplement the fundamental note of any given meridian, therefore—to lift or "raise" its energies—we must go *below* it in the scale and play its lower fifth. In this sense, the lower fifth "donates" its energy to the higher note in much the same way that the mother gives away her energies to her child in the Generation Cycle. Drainage, of course, is just the opposite; it is a reduction or "lowering" of the energy. To drain the fundamental, therefore, we "lower" its energies by going *above* it in the scale to play its upper major third. In effect, the upper major third drains the fundamental like the child drains the mother in the Generation Cycle.

As we learned in chapters 1 and 2, the perfect fifth and major third are contained within the first five harmonics. They are a natural component of the series of partials found within any note. Figure 6.1 shows the first six harmonics for a fundamental of $F^\#_4$. The perfect fifth ($C^\#_5$) is at the 3rd harmonic and the major third ($A^\#_6$) is at the 5th harmonic.

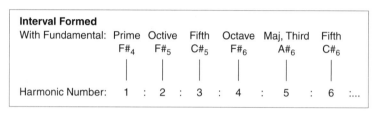

Figure 6.1 Internal/Harmonic Relationship

Now look closely at the position of the perfect fifth: it is midway between $F^\#_5$ and its higher octave, $F^\#_6$, represented by "3" in the series 2 : 3 : 4. The perfect fifth, therefore, is the harmonic midpoint in the process of raising the octave, and this is a graphic demonstration of its augmenting, supplementing properties. The major third is midway between $F^\#_6$ and its upper fifth, $C^\#_6$, represented by "5" in the series 4: 5: 6. It is the harmonic midpoint, therefore, in the movement from the fundamental to its upper fifth. It represents a draining of energy from the fundamental, since—as we have just seen—it is the natural tendency of any note in a scale to donate its energies to the fifth above it.

Table 6.1 displays the fundamental, lower fifth, and upper major third for each of the twelve meridians. A quick glance at this Table raises an important question: how can we supply upper third's and lower fifth's to all twelve notes if we have only one octave of tuning forks? As shown in Figure 6.2, the upper major third's of A, A# and B are above the scale of the tuning forks, while the lower fifth's of C#, D, D# E, F and F# are below it.

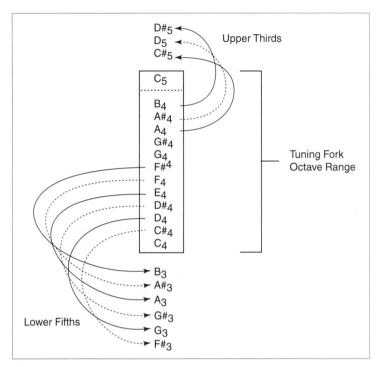

Figure 6.2 Diagram Showing Upper Third's and Lower Fifth's Outside Range of Tuning Fork Octave

In practice, we can make use of only one octave of tuning forks if we understand the principles of the harmonic series just described. By recognizing that any note contains a sequence of higher notes within it, we can allow the necessary intervals to form on a harmonic level. If we need to supplement the Liver meridian, for example, we will need the $F^{\#}_4$-fork and its lower fifth. Referring to Figure 6.2, the lower fifth of $F^{\#}_4$ is B_3. Since the B_4 tuning fork contained in our set is higher than $F^{\#}_4$, it will form an upper fourth with this note, not a lower fifth. Now look again at Figure 6.1. Note that the 2nd harmonic of $F^{\#}_4$ is its higher octave: $F^{\#}_5$. Since B_4 is a 5th below $F^{\#}_5$, *the two tuning forks will create the necessary interval on the harmonic level.*

The same principles will work for the upper major third. If we need to drain the Stomach meridian, for example, will need the

A_4-fork and its upper major third. Referring again to Figure 6.2, the upper major third of A_4 is $C^\#_5$. The $C^\#_4$ tuning fork that comes with our set is lower than A_4; it will form a lower minor sixth with this note, not an upper major third. But the 2nd harmonic of $C^\#_4$ is its higher octave, $C^\#_5$, which is a major third above A_4. Thus, the two tuning forks are once again creating the necessary interval on the harmonic level.

While it is true that tuning forks are designed to limit partials (see Chapter 2), it is almost impossible to completely eliminate the first partial (i.e., the second harmonic), which is always the next octave above the fundamental. Furthermore, partials are certain to be generated once the tuning fork or forks touch the skin and the frequencies begin to resonate through the cellular fluids. Thus, the body will still receive the correct Acutone message, even if the notes appear to be coming from the "wrong" octave. The student should therefore ignore the octave of the tuning fork frequency, and simply select the fork that matches the required treatment note according to Table 6.1.

Lower		Upper Major	
Meridian	Fifth	Fundamental	Third
TW	A	E	G#
Pc	G#	D#	G
Ki	G	D	F#
UB	F#	C#	F
SI	F	C	E
Ht	E	B	D#
Sp	D#	A#	D
St	D	A	C#
LI	C#	G#	C
Lu	C	G	B
Liv	B	F#	A#
GB	A#	F	A

Table 6.1 Perfect Fifths and Major Thirds

2. Guidelines for Musculo-Skeletal Treatment

Let us now go through the treatment of a single-meridian musculoskeletal problem. In our first example, we will address a case of shoulder pain. We shall assume that the overall distribution of pain indicates that the local meridian most responsible for the problem is the Triple Warmer, and the primary tissue involved is *sinew*.

Step 1: Plan the treatment, selecting the appropriate local and distal points. Locate and mark all the selected points.

Example: Shoulder pain. Primary causative meridian: Triple Warmer. Distant point: TW 5. Local points: TW 15, TW 14, GB 21.

Step 2: Consult Table 6.1: the tuning fork that matches the fundamental of the affected meridian will be the primary fork used to treat it.

Example: The fundamental for the Triple Warmer meridian is **E**. So the E-fork will become the primary fork we will use in treating this meridian.

Step 3: Next pick the secondary fork. Determine whether you intend to supplement or drain the meridian. If you are draining the meridian, pick the tone that is the major third above the fundamental; if you are supplementing, pick the perfect fifth below it.

Example: The condition is one of excess, and we intend to drain the Triple Warmer. Our secondary fork, therefore, will need to be a major third above E. Consulting Table 6.1 we see that this note is **G#**. The E-fork will be the primary fork and the G#-fork secondary.

Step 4: Pick the first point you intend to treat. Hold the primary fork in the right hand and the secondary fork in the left hand (reverse if left-handed). Strike both forks, then lower the stem of the primary fork toward the selected point. Make sure you are using the correct supplementation or drainage techniques described in Chapter 2. Once contact with the skin has been made, lower the secondary fork until its stem is slightly above the prongs of the primary fork. The two tuning forks will form a straight line (Figure 4.1). Be careful not to let the two tuning forks touch.

Example: The selected treatment point of the Triple Warmer meridian is TW 5. Hold the E-fork in the right hand and the G#-fork in the left. Since we are using draining technique, strike both forks loudly. Lower the stem of the E-fork to TW 5 rapidly. When contact has been made with the skin, press a little bit harder, but not too hard. Now lower the stem of the G#-fork until it is just above the prongs of the E-fork.

Step 5: Hold both forks steady until the correct supplementing or draining stimulus has been delivered, then withdraw the second fork and palm or pocket it. Then withdraw the primary fork using the correct supplementing or draining technique.

Example: We are using draining technique, so we withdraw the G#-fork while the tone of the E-fork is still ringing. Palm or pocket the G# fork. Then slowly withdraw the stem of the E-fork leaving the "hole" open.

Step 6: Now we will treat the local points. Select the tuning fork which best matches the tissue being targeted. *Important*: when treating local points, we must select the tone from the *pentatonic* scale according to the rules outlined in Chapter 2.

Example: We have determined that the problem is in the sinews. The sinews are ruled by Wood, so we select the A# tuning fork. We treat each of the selected local points—TW 15, TW 14, GB 21—with drainage technique, as explained in Chapter 2.

Options for Supplementing or Draining the Meridian

There are actually many ways of doing the treatment just described. Listed below are some options.

- We can supplement or drain the targeted meridian with two distant points instead of one. To do this you must decide which point is the primary treatment point. Always place the primary fork on the primary point first, the secondary fork on the secondary point second, and withdraw in reverse order. Use the necessary supplementation and drainage technique.

Example: We decide to drain the Triple Warmer with TW 5 and TW 6. We choose TW 5 as the primary point. We hold one fork in each hand as before, and strike both forks loudly. We rapidly lower the E-fork to TW 5, followed by G# on TW 6. While the E-fork is still vibrating, slowly withdraw the G#-fork first, and then the E-fork, leaving the holes open at both points.

- We can use the secondary fork to stroke the meridian while the primary fork is held at the treatment point.

Example: We have decided to drain the Triple Warmer meridian as above, and our primary treatment point is TW 5. We hold one fork in each hand and strike both forks loudly. We rapidly lower the E-fork to TW 5, and while holding it on the point, we stroke the Triple Warmer meridian with the G#-fork. Since we are draining, we will stroke against the flow of the meridian (i.e., distally).

- Using the same techniques described above, we can drain the main meridian and supplement the local points, or we can supplement the main meridian and drain the local points. This will require that we follow the rules of *meridian sinew treatment*, too complex to describe here. We recommend the reader consult *Practical Application of Meridian-Style*

Acupuncture by John Pirog, which explains the technique in detail.

- We can select distant points from more than one meridian. You must supplement or drain these additional meridian(s) using the same rules as described for the main meridian.

Example: Since the local points TW 14, TW 15, and GB 21 are focused in the Shao Yang region, we decide to add a distal point on the Gall Bladder meridian, GB 39. Referring to Table 6.1, we choose F as the primary tuning fork. Since we intend to drain the Gall Bladder meridian, we select A, the upper major third, as the secondary tuning fork. We then repeat the process of Step 4 above. Hold the F-fork in the right hand and the A-fork in the left. Since we are using draining technique, strike both forks loudly. Lower the stem of the F-fork to GB 39 rapidly. When contact has been made with the skin, press a little bit harder, but not too hard. Now lower the stem of the A-fork until it is just above the prongs of the F-fork.

Options for Supplementing and Draining Local Points

- We can drain some local points and supplement others, depending on the findings on each point. In general, loose weak tissue is deficient while hard strong tissue is excess.

- We can select the tone for local points based on the prevailing pathogen (see Chapter 2)

Example: If the patient's shoulder is very stiff and pain is worse in rainy weather, we might surmise that the condition is caused by exogenous damp, in which case the local points will be treated with F#, the Earth tone.

- We can select the tone for local points based on depth of *kori* or pressure pain (see Chapter 2).

Example: If the kori's, for example, are found at the superficial level, we use G#. If pain is elicited by deep pressure, we can use D#.

- We can drain a point at the superficial level with one fork, and then pick a different fork to treat the deeper levels.

Example: Let's say that palpation of GB 21 reveals a superficial kori, but deeper palpation indicates tightness in the deeper sinews. We would drain the surface with G#, and then we would use A# to disperse the deeper layers of tissue.

- We can use stroking or trilling (see Chapter 2) to treat the general area.

- We can combine any of the methods described above, varying the technique according to the different palpatory findings at each point.

Example:

- Begin by trilling the general area with G# to remove superficial wind.

- TW 14: Pain at the bone level, local tissues deficient: Supplement with D#.

- TW 15: Signs of excess dampness: Drain with F#.

- GB 21: Hard, excess-type kori on surface level, weakness in deeper sinews: Drain with G#, then supplement with A#.

3. Guidelines for Internal Treatment

In case the twelve-meridian system is used to treat a deeper health problem, the following guidelines should be used. As an example, we will be treating a patient with dysmenorrhea due to qi and blood deficiency. Our point selection is based on the treatment described in *Chinese Acupuncture and Moxabustion*. [40]

---

[40] Cheng Xinnong, p. 452.

Step 1: Plan the treatment by selecting the meridians you wish to target. Next select the treatment points. Locate and mark the points.

Example: Menstrual pain due to qi and blood deficiency. Targeted meridians: Spleen, Stomach, and Conception Vessel. Selected points: Sp 6, St 36, CV 4, UB 20.

Step 2: Decide which meridian is most important to the treatment, and select the tuning fork that corresponds with this meridian's fundamental note according to Table 7.1. This will be the primary fork used to treat this meridian.

Example: Let's say we've determined that the Spleen is the most important meridian. Referring to Table 6.1, we see that the fundamental for the Spleen meridian is **A#**. So the A#-fork will become the primary fork we will use in treating this meridian.

Step 3: Next select the secondary fork. Determine whether you intend to supplement or drain the meridian. If you are draining the meridian, pick the tone that is the major third above the fundamental; if you are supplementing, pick the perfect fifth below.

Example. The fundamental for the Spleen meridian is A#. Since we intend to supplement it, we will need the perfect fifth below A#. Consulting Table 6.1, we see that this note is **D#**. The A#-fork will therefore be the primary fork and the D#-fork secondary.

Step 4: Pick the first point you intend to treat. Hold the primary fork in the right hand and the secondary fork in the left hand (reverse if left-handed). Strike both forks then lower the stem of the primary fork toward the selected point. Make sure you are using the correct supplementation or drainage techniques described in Chapter 2. Once contact with the skin has been made, lower the second fork until its stem is slightly above the prongs of the primary fork. The two tuning forks will form a straight line (Figure 4.1). Be careful not to let the two tuning forks touch.

Example: Hold the A#-fork in the right hand and the D#-fork in the left. Strike both forks and slowly lower the stem of the A# fork to Sp 6. Then lower the D# fork until its stem is just above the prongs of the A# fork.

Step 5: Hold both forks steady until the tone of the primary fork has almost completely died out. Now withdraw the second fork and palm it in your hand. Then rapidly withdraw the primary fork while simultaneously "closing" the point with the index finger of the free hand (Figure 4.2).

Example: When the tone of the A#-fork has almost completely died out, withdraw the D#-fork, and palm or pocket it. Then place your left index finger on the edge of the stem of the A#-fork and withdraw rapidly while firmly pressing down on Sp 6 with the left index finger.

Step 6: If you have only selected one meridian for treatment, you can skip this step altogether and proceed to step 8. To treat the second meridian you have selected, repeat steps 5 and 6 above, selecting the necessary tones for the new meridian and supplementing or draining as needed. Continue this procedure on all the meridians that have been chosen for the treatment.

Example: On the treatment in question, our second selected meridian is the Stomach, and we have chosen to treat St 36. Consulting Table 6.1, our primary fork will be **A**, the fundamental tone for the Stomach. The second fork will be D, a fifth below A. Holding the A-fork in the right hand and the D fork in the left hand, strike both forks and slowly lower the stem of the A-fork to St 36 using supplementation technique. Then lower the D-fork until its stem is just above the prongs of the A-fork (Figure 4.1). When the vibration has nearly died out, withdraw the D-fork and palm or pocket it. Then place your left index finger next to the stem of the A-fork and withdraw rapidly while closing the exposed point with the index finger (Figure 4.2).

Step 7: Select the correct note for each local point. When we treat local points, we must return to the rules of local treatment selection, and choose the *pentatonic note*, i.e., the five-phase note, that corresponds with the organ being treated at each point.

Example: In this case we have selected CV 4 and UB 20. Assuming we start with CV 4, we must decide which of the three meridians intersecting this point we want to access. Since the underlying cause of qi and blood deficiency is usually Spleen qi deficiency, we select the Spleen. Since we are using CV 4 to access the Spleen organ, we have to use the pentatonic note for the Earth phase, not the chromatic note for the Spleen meridian. The tone of the Earth phase is F#, and this is the tuning fork we will use on CV 4. This same tone will also be used to treat UB 20, since this later is the shu-back point of the Spleen. Let us reemphasize that we are now treating the Spleen organ, not the Spleen meridian, so the selected note will not be same as the chromatic note we used earlier to treat Sp 6.

Step 8: Treat each of the selected local points with its corresponding pentatonic note. Use supplementation or drainage technique as required. Remember that only one tone can be used at a time on local points.

Example: Beginning with CV 4, strike the F#-fork and relocate the point with the left index finger. Turn the index finger at right angles while holding it on the point, being careful not to press too hard. With the right hand, slowly lower the stem of the F#-fork until it contacts the skin. When the vibration has nearly died out, withdraw the fork quickly with the right hand while pressing on the point with the index finger of the left hand (Figure 4.2). Repeat this procedure on UB 20.

Options:

Once again, there are several variations to the above treatment.

- Instead of holding two forks above a single point, it is possible to select *two points* on the primary meridian. The primary tuning fork should be placed on the point which is most crucial to the treatment, and the secondary fork should be placed on the supporting point (Figure 4.3). Apply the primary fork to the primary treatment point *first*, and the secondary fork to the supporting point *second*. Withdraw the forks in the reverse order. Use supplementation or drainage technique as required.

Example: To supplement the Spleen meridian, we have selected Sp 6 as the primary treatment point and Sp 4 as the secondary point. Hold the A#- and D#-forks in each hand as before. Strike both forks and begin by slowly lowering the stem of A# to Sp 6. As soon as it contacts the skin, hold it in place while lowering D# to Sp 4 with the opposite hand. Hold both forks motionless on the two points. When the vibration of A# has almost died out, hold it in place while quickly withdrawing D# from Sp 4. Palm or pocket the D#-fork, then use the index finger of the free hand to close the hole on Sp 6 while rapidly withdrawing the A#-fork. Since you only have two hands, you will only be able to close the hole of the main treatment point.

- Supplementation and drainage can be combined for a more comprehensive treatment.

Example: Let us shift our diagnosis to dysmenorrhea due to Liver-Spleen Disharmony. In this case, the pain will be more severe, and the Liver meridian will be excess and the Spleen meridian deficient. First we will supplement the Spleen and Stomach meridians, following the steps described above. Next we will drain the Liver meridian. Let us suppose we have chosen Liv 3 as the treatment point. Consulting Table 6.1, we choose the notes F# and its upper major third, A#, and we drain Liv 3 using the techniques already described. Since there is much pain in the lower abdomen, we might choose to drain CV 4 with A#, the pentatonic note for the Liver meridian, while supplementing UB 20 with F# as above.

4. A Word About Local Treatment

The reader will notice that the tone selection for local points described in this Chapter is essentially the same as the tone selection described in the five-phase Acutone treatment in Chapter 4. In each case, the notes selected for local treatment come from the pentatonic scale. When using the twelve-meridian system, therefore, one must use the notes of the chromatic scale to treat the *meridians*, while the notes of the pentatonic scale are used on local points. This is because the targets of the local points are tissues, pathogens, or internal organs, and all of these are governed by the symbol structure of the five-phases.

While the two systems of twelve-meridian and five-phase Acutone have their own distinctive diagnostic principles and treatment rules, the treatment principles of local points remains the same. Even when the bodily energy is organized along the principles of the twelve-meridian *Zi-Wu* cycle, we cannot completely escape the more primitive symbolism of the five-phases.

Chapter VII

Auxiliary Techniques and Case Histories

1. Auxiliary Techniques

We urge the reader to master the basic methodologies of Acutone before experimenting with the accessory techniques described in this chapter. It is important to understand that the forgoing modalities have been designed for *local treatment only*. They should be part of a more comprehensive treatment plan that includes root treatment—supplementation or drainage of the meridians—with the basic Acutone techniques outlined in chapters 4 and 6. In most circumstances, root treatment is best accomplished non-invasively, with tuning forks alone. Local treatment, however, can perhaps be augmented with the addition of other modalities such as acupuncture and Piezo-electric crystals. Listed below are a few of the techniques that the two authors have found particularly useful.

• *"Upside Down" Technique with Needles*

There are some circumstances where the practitioner might desire to combine Acutone treatment with the stronger stimulus provided by acupuncture needles. Examples include localized blood stasis or stubborn *bi* patterns in patients with otherwise robust constitutions, where a stronger draining effect is called for. One way to combine tone therapy with acupuncture is to stimulate the inserted needles indirectly, using the air as a vibrating medium. We refer to this as the "Upside Down" Acutone technique.

Begin by locating the point and inserting the needle using the appropriate supplementation or drainage technique. Next choose a tuning fork based on the local treatment principles outlined in Chapter 2. Now strike the fork and lower it "upside down" (i.e., with prongs pointed downward) over the inserted needle (Figure 7.1). The fork should be lowered until the handle of the needle is positioned between the two vibrating prongs. The prongs should not touch the needle, and the tuning fork should form a straight line with the needle. You can carefully raise and lower the tuning fork in a kind of lift-and-thrust motion to enhance the effect. After the treatment is complete, withdraw the needle using the appropriate supplementation or drainage method.

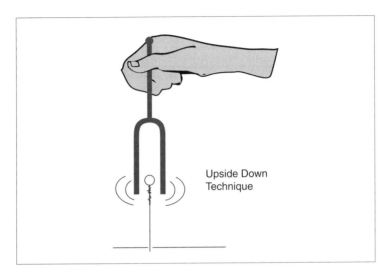

Figure 7.1 Upside Down Technique

When using the Upside Down technique, supplementation or drainage of the point is accomplished mainly through insertion, withdrawal, and manipulation of the needle itself rather than through manipulation of the fork.

• *Press Tacks*

Another way to combine needle insertion with Acutone is through the use of *press tacks*. Press tacks are tiny needles shaped like thumbtacks (Figure 7.2), designed to be left in place after treatment. Their penetration depth is generally quite shallow, between 1 and 2 millimeters. Once the tack is inserted, the looped handle is flush with the skin. In order to apply press tacks, first clean the insertion area thoroughly with an alcohol swab. With freshly cleaned hands, locate and mark the point. Insert the press tack into the selected point with sterile forceps; making sure that the needle penetrates the skin vertically. Once the insertion has been made, cover the top of the press tack with tape. Some brands of disposable press tacks come with tape already attached to the needle head. It is possible to insert several press tacks into the same region during one treatment.

After the tack is in place and covered with tape, simply press the stem of the vibrating tuning fork directly onto the needle, using any of the techniques described in Chapter 2 (Figure 7.2). The press tacks can be removed at the end of the treatment, or, if the practitioner desires, they can be left in place for up to three days. Since bodily serum can wick up the edge of the needle shaft, it is important to cover the head of the press tack with tape before touching it with the tuning fork stem. This will prevent the stem of the tuning fork from becoming contaminated.

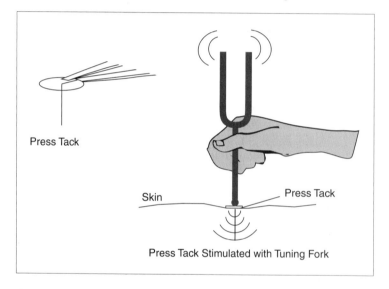

Press Tack

Skin

Press Tack

Press Tack Stimulated with Tuning Fork

Figure 7.2 Press Tack Technique

• *Magraine Pellets*

"Magraine pellets" (also referred to as "ion pellets" or "B-B's") are tiny steel balls. Some versions are plated with silver or gold. They are usually sold in small peel-away sheets with attached tape. Because of their minute size, these pellets can produce a stronger, sharper stimulus of the skin than is possible with the rather blunt bottom of a tuning fork stem. Furthermore, the silver and gold contained in plated pellets is believed to have supplementing properties. To apply Magraine pellets, locate and

mark the points as above, and press the taped pellet onto the point. The tuning fork can then be used to stimulate the point using any of the techniques described in Chapter 2 (Figure 7.3).

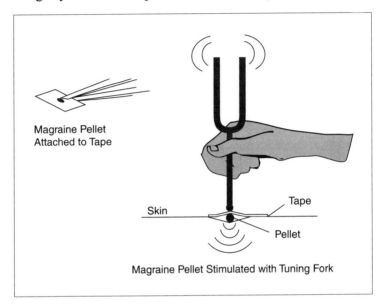

Magraine Pellet
Attached to Tape

Skin

Tape

Pellet

Magraine Pellet Stimulated with Tuning Fork

Figure 7.3 Pellet Technique

Magraine pellets can also be useful in the treatment of palpable masses and tumors, using an acupuncture technique called "Surround the Dragon." Begin by completely surrounding the circumference of the tumor with pellets, placing them about a centimeter apart (Figure 7.4). After selecting the appropriate tuning fork, go around the tumor and stimulate each of the pellets as described above.

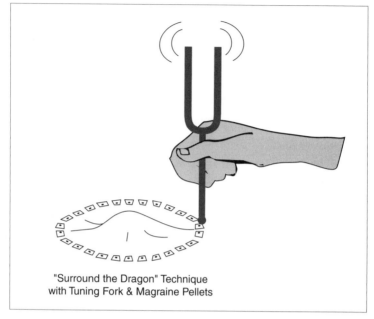

"Surround the Dragon" Technique
with Tuning Fork & Magraine Pellets

Figure 7.4 Pellet Technique, Surrounding the Dragon

The tuning fork should be selected according to the nature of the lesion. Phlegm nodules, for example, can be treated with F# (the tone for Earth, which is associated with dampness and phlegm), while tumors due to blood stasis can be treated with C# (the tone for the capillaries) or A# (the tone for the Liver, which has the function of assisting the flow of blood). Bone spurs and deep tumors that feel hard like rocks can be treated with D# (the tone for the Kidney and the bones).

Note: This technique is inappropriate for boils, carbuncles and other local infections, or "hot" tumors with localized redness, warmth and swelling.

Once the treatment is completed, the pellets can be left attached to the body. *Steel pellets should never remain on the same point for more than 24 hours.* Pellets left on the skin too long can penetrate through the epidermis, especially during the summer when the skin is hydrated from increased perspiration. Every time a pellet is removed, a slight indentation will be left on the skin, and the next pellet should be placed on intact skin nearby. So long as the patient understands that he must change the pellets daily and vary their location, he can continue to administer the therapy himself at home.

• *Crystals*

Quartz crystals are naturally-occurring hexagonal crystals composed of silicon dioxide (SiO_2). They can be purchased at rock collector's shops or "New Age" bookstores. Quartz crystals have attracted the authors' attention because they resonate well with tuning forks and because they have Piezo-electric properties that can convert acoustic vibration into electrical energy. Quartz crystals seem to be especially useful in the treatment of neuropathies and deep *bi* patterns where cold pathogens have settled deep into the bones.

Crystals and precious stones have long been the subject of romance and metaphysical speculation. We are assuming for the present discussion that these artifacts are not magic wands but medical instruments like any other, their effectiveness dependent mainly on skillful utilization. We recommend the use of crude crystals that have not been cut or polished. A crystal need not look aesthetically pleasing to be suitable for treatment. For Acutone purposes, the best crystals are small and quite thin—one to three inches long and no more than 1/2 inch thick. "Double terminated" crystals, which have naturally occurring points on both ends, are the most effective (Figure 7.5A). It is usually the narrower end that is placed on the skin.

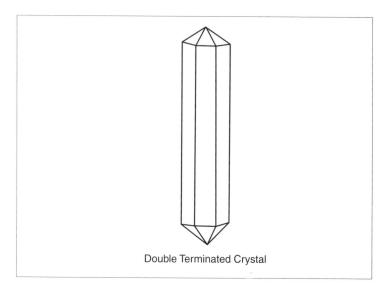

Double Terminated Crystal

Figure 7.5A Crystal

Based on our experience, crystals work best after they are first lightly heated over a candle or lamp flame (Figure 7.5B). The crystal should be heated just enough so it can be held in the fingers without burning. We naturally want to avoid injuring the patient, but we also want to avoid lowering the acoustic frequency being sent through the crystal, which can result if the crystal's temperature is raised too high.

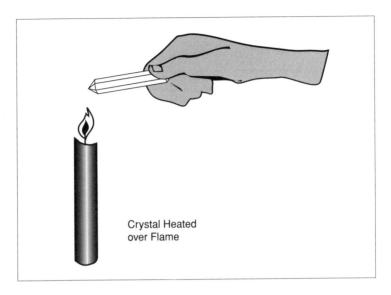

Crystal Heated
over Flame

Figure 7.5B Crystal Using Flame

Begin by locating and marking all the treatment points. Hold the freshly warmed crystal and the selected tuning fork in the right hand (reverse if left-handed). Place the index or middle finger of the left hand over the selected point and then turn the finger at right angles to expose the point. Then lower the crystal between the thumb and fingers and press gently until it contacts skin (Figure 7.5C). The crystal should still be quite warm to the touch. Try to adjust the index finger, middle finger, and thumb so that they completely seal off and surround the bottom of the crystal contacting the skin.

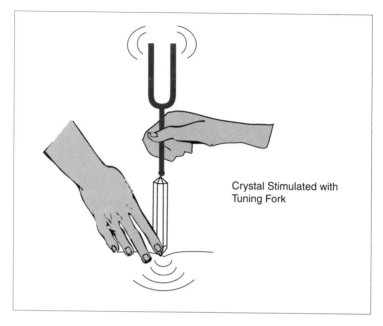

Crystal Stimulated with Tuning Fork

Figure 7.5C Tuning Fork With Crystal

Next, strike the tuning fork and place the stem firmly on the exposed tip of the crystal. The vibration should be clearly felt with the fingers of the left hand as it passes through the crystal. The tuning fork can be applied up to three times on the same point. When the crystal is withdrawn, the exposed point can be closed with the index finger of the right hand or left open as the treatment requires (see Chapter 2).

• *The Resonance Bell*

The Resonance Bell can be used to radiate a tone wherever the practitioner desires. It can be swept across the lengths of meridians, circled around large areas, or held focused on individual points. In order to create a sustained frequency, the Resonance Bell requires the use of two forks of the same tone (see Chapter 2), and this necessitates that you have two identical sets of tuning forks on hand. However, if only one fork is available, the technique may still be performed. A box using one fork with the configuration most suitable for each note may be used instead of the resonance bell (Figure 7.6A). Plucking the forks prong's just before the tone dies out, one may get results almost as effective as the technique described above

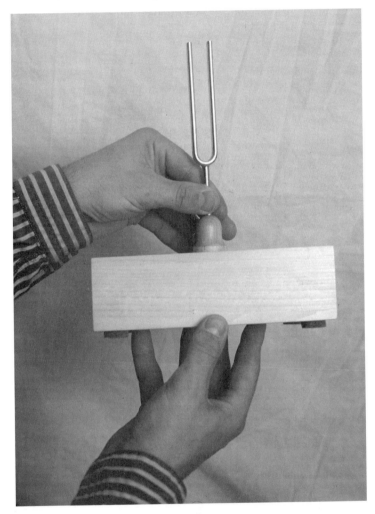

Figure 7.6A Standard Resonance Box

Select two forks of the appropriate frequency and hold them firmly in the notches on top of the Bell with the thumb of one hand. Alternately pinch the prongs of each fork while holding the Bell several inches above the point or area selected for treatment. Continue to pinch the forks so that a sustained tone is sent into the selected site. This technique is particularly effective when used on Mu-Alarm and Shu-Back points. It can also be used to stimulate inserted acupuncture needles (Figure 7.6B). See Appendix D for retail sources for the Resonance Bell.

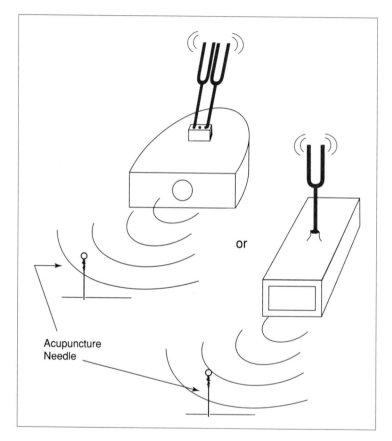

Acupuncture
Needle

or

Figure 7.6B Resonance Bell

• *Lower Octave Tuning Forks*

Lower-octave tuning forks are very effective in treating local points on fuller-bodied patients or in patients of robust constitution where stronger stimulus is needed to drain stagnant excess. Tuning forks with frequencies below C_4 have much greater mass and therefore emit more powerful vibrations. Since lower-octave tuning forks are used exclusively in local treatment, only the five notes of the pentatonic scale are needed ($C\#_3$, $D\#_3$, $F\#_3$, $G\#_3$, and $A\#_3$). They are used in exactly the same manner as regular tuning forks when performing local treatment. Lower octave tuning forks should not be used in root treatment, i.e., in supplementing or draining of meridians, since their overly strong vibrations will cause unwanted dispersion of the meridian energy. See Appendix D for retail sources for lower-octave tuning fork sets.

2. Case Histories

We have chosen, with perhaps some hesitation, to share a few case histories from our private practices. We fully recognize that anecdotal cases such as those presented below do not necessarily "prove" the veracity or our theories nor do they verify the effectiveness of our methods. We are including them here in an effort to enhance our reader's ability to understand and employ the techniques described in this book, and not to create an artificial aura of credibility. Like any other form of energic healing, one must prove Acutone for one's self, and results are certain to vary according to the technique's compatibility with the personality and skill of the practitioner as well as the needs of the patient.

So many writers in our field, when recording case histories from their personal practices, include only their successes and omit failures. Furthermore, the impression is created that the patients so described have all gone on to live happily ever after. Those of you who have been in private practice for a long time know that this is rarely if ever true, especially when the practitioner is confronted with chronic degenerative illness. Even in the most successful cases, chronically sick patients can fall back into illness after they have left our care. In other cases, the therapy fails altogether; or the credit for the results is ambivalent, as when several different forms of intervention are mixed together in the same patient.

The authors certainly look forward to doing objective scientific studies with Acutone in the future. But for the time being, we must all be content to learn this system the way we learned the other techniques in our practice, through careful observation of the impact it has made on our patients' lives, building on the successes and learning from the failures. And so we have taken pains to describe our experiences with Acutone as truthfully as possible, making sure to include a couple of instances where the results were disappointing. In some of the following cases, Acutone was the only therapy employed, while in others it was used as an adjunct to additional interventions, including herbs, acupuncture, massage, and Western medications. As you will see, it can make a positive and decisive impact in the treatment of many people, but not all.

Case History 1: Low Back Pain

Practitioner: Dean Lloyd
Diagnostic Paradigm: Modern Chinese
Acutone Treatment Methodology: Local Acutone combined with acupuncture using the pentatonic scale

A 41 year-old male construction worker, 6' 1", 197 lbs., suffered from lower back pain due to a herniated L5 disc caused by a lifting injury 20 years earlier. The pain was aggravated by a job that required frequent bending and lifting. Over the last 7 years, the patient had made use of Tylenol and chiropractic treatment to control pain.

When the patient came to see me he was experiencing a dull ache in the area between UB 22 and UB 25. The pain level was "8" (1-10). In addition, sharp pain was felt at 50 grams of pressure at UB 22.

Pulse: wiry
Tongue: slightly purple, uncoated
Diagnosis: Cold *Bi* Pattern with localized blood stasis

Treatment:
Acupuncture needles were placed in-situ bilaterally at UB 22, UB 23, UB 25 and UB 60. I selected the D# tuning fork because of the location of all the treatment points on the Water-ruled Urinary Bladder meridian, and also because of the fact that it was a cold *bi* pattern and the problem seemed to be located at the bone level. After the needles were inserted, I stimulated them with the "Upside Down" method described earlier in this Chapter. The fork was held over each point for about 20 seconds for two rounds during a 20-minute session.

After the treatment, the patient stated that the relief was better than any therapy he had previously tried. His pain level had dropped to "2" (1-10) and the sharp pressure pain at UB 22 had disappeared. The patient has continued to see me once or twice a month for maintenance therapy. Using a mixture of Acutone, acupuncture, and Shiatsu, I have managed to keep his pain under control in spite of his continued employment in a job that is physically demanding.

Case History 2: Control of Nausea and Pain in Patient Undergoing Cancer Chemotherapy

Practitioner: John Pirog
Diagnostic Paradigm: Five-phase
Acutone Treatment Method: Five-phase Acutone root and local treatment using the pentatonic scale, with Magraine pellets as an accessory technique, together with Chinese herbs.

A 56 year old woman, 5' 5", 122 lbs., presented with severe ascites and multiple metastatic abdominal tumors from ovarian cancer. Ten years earlier, she had had a mastectomy for breast cancer. Since her current tumors were too large and numerous for surgery, her physicians had opted to begin treatment with chemotherapy. While her extremities were emaciated, the distention in her abdomen was severe enough to yield nearly 2 liters of fluid when aspirated. Once some of the fluid had been drained, several fist-sized masses became palpable in the upper left, upper right, and lower left abdominal quadrants. She nevertheless had very little abdominal pain, although her stools were frequent and slightly loose. She complained of mild night sweats, but did not feel hot or restless. Until very recently, she had continued to work part time in an office located in her home.

Pulse: deep, thready, deficient in the Kidney and Lung position.
Tongue: bright red, uncoated in the anterior portion, very light greasy yellow coat in the posterior.
Five-phase root diagnosis: Kidney Deficiency Pattern.

Treatment:
The treatment plan in my office required twice-weekly visits together with the prescription of a Chinese herbal formula designed to drain damp, tonify qi and yin, remove toxic heat and dispel blood stasis. The patient simultaneously received chemotherapy every other week; during the intervening weeks Epogen was administered to boost white blood cell count. Each session in my clinic would involve reformulation of the herbal prescription together with administration of Acutone.

The Acutone treatment consisted of supplementation of the Kidney meridian at Ki 3 or Ki 7 with D# (the tone for Water) as the primary fork, and G# (the tone for Metal) as the secondary fork. The Lung meridian was then supplemented at Lu 5 with G# alone. Because the pulse was quite weak, I elected not to do any drainage at all in the beginning.

Over a period of several weeks, the abdominal swelling gradually receded, the night sweating ceased, and the tongue became less red. A light white and slightly greasy coat gradually returned to the anterior aspect of the tongue. As the patient's condition improved, I was able to focus a local treatment on the abdominal tumors, which were now more easily palpated. I used the "Surround the Dragon" technique with gold-plated Magraine pellets, encircling the two most prominent tumors on the upper left and lower left quadrant. Because of the great depth of the tumors, and because of the root deficiency in the Kidneys, I chose to stimulate the pellets with D#. I used a mixture of supplementing and draining technique, occasionally reinforcing the tuning fork stimulus with a heated quartz crystal. The patient was shown how to circle the tumors with the pellets, and continued to replaced them daily at home.

When the patient complained of nausea after chemotherapy sessions, I would add local dispersion of CV 12 with F#, together with self-administered finger pressure on P 6, together with adjustment of the ingredients of the herbal formula. The administration of Epogen sometimes caused aching in the bones, which was relieved by drainage of GV 14 and UB 11 (the meeting point for bones) using D#.

Over the following months, the size of the tumors gradually shrank, until after six months of therapy they were no longer palpable. The blood stasis dispelling and damp-draining herbs were gradually removed from the formula, and I focused on supplementation of qi and blood. The Acutone root treatment remained the same. When I could no longer find any tumors, I replaced the local abdominal treatment with direct moxa on UB 17 and UB 19.

Nine months later, after completing several rounds of chemotherapy, the patient's CA-125 readings had returned to normal and her tumors were undetectable in CAT scans. Although she had lost her hair during the early weeks of chemotherapy, this gradually returned after chemotherapy was discontinued. At the present writing, one year after beginning therapy, the patient has returned to work and continues to see me twice a month for maintenance, where I continue to administer Acutone root treatment as described above, together with a lower dosage of Chinese herbs.

Comment:

In my opinion, this patient's recovery—which surpassed everyone's expectations, including her oncologist's—was primarily due to the simultaneous administration of Western chemotherapy and Chinese herbs. There is no doubt, however, that the Acutone was effective in controlling bone pain and nausea, allowing the chemotherapy to proceed smoothly and without interruption. The patient was too weak in the beginning for conventional acupuncture, and the gentleness of Acutone made this therapy a very effective substitute.

Case History 3: Headache

Practitioner: Dean Lloyd
Diagnostic Paradigm: Modern Chinese
Acutone Treatment Methodology: Twelve-meridian Acutone using the chromatic scale in root treatment, pentatonic scale in local treatment

An 8 year old girl, 4' 10", 70 lbs., was brought to the clinic complaining of frequent headaches in the temples. Medical follow-up had found no cause for the headaches. In addition, the child would experience several episodes of hiccups a week, each lasting 20 minutes or more, usually occurring after meals. Finally, the child had almost daily emotional outbursts, where she would scream and throw objects at slight annoyances.

Tongue: red at tip and body with light coat in the center.
Pulse: moderate
Diagnosis: Liver Invading Stomach

Treatment:

It has been my experience that children respond quickly to Acutone therapy. In this case, I was delighted to see results with just four points: Liv 3, St 36, St 37, and Tai Yang. I began by draining Liv 3. In the twelve-meridian Acutone scale, the Liver meridian is ruled by F#; so I selected F# as the primary fork and A# (the upper major third of F#), as the secondary fork. I used both forks on Liv 3 simultaneously, with F# touching the point and A# held above it.

Next I dispersed the Stomach meridian. The Stomach meridian is ruled by A, so I selected A as the primary fork and C# (the upper major third of A) as the secondary fork. Using draining technique, I applied the A fork to St 36 and the C# fork to St 37.

Next I turned my attention to local treatment. I decided to treat Tai Yang with A#, the pentatonic tone for Wood. This decision was made in part because Tai Yang is located at the juncture of tendon and bone. Furthermore, the root condition could be seen as a Liver problem, and Tai Yang can be viewed as an extra point on the trajectory of the Gall Bladder meridian. In order to soften the stimulus, I placed my index finger over Tai Yang and gently applied the tuning fork over my fingernail using draining technique (see Chapter 2 for an explanation of this technique).

The child became more calm during the session. Later, her mother reported that she was able to sleep without complaining of pain that night. A few days later, she had another headache and asked her mother if she could be taken for more of "the tone treatment." Over a course of 3 weekly sessions, the hiccup spells and headaches gradually receded until after three months, they occur only rarely. The child no longer has emotional outbursts.

Case History 4: Dermatitis

Practitioner: Dean Lloyd
Diagnostic Paradigm: Modern Chinese
Acutone Treatment Methodology: Twelve-meridian Acutone using the chromatic scale in both root and local treatment.

A 42 year-old woman presented with weeping skin eruptions in her lower extremities, diagnosed as dermatitis by her dermatologist. Continuous scratching had left broken skin with a purplish bruised look. In addition, for the last three months there had been an increase in the length of her periods, with bleeding that lasted as much as 11 days. She also complained of weak limbs, a loss of her sense of taste, and a craving for sweets.

Pulse: soft and rapid
Tongue: bluish body with thin clean white coat
Lips: purple
Diagnosis: Spleen Qi Deficiency causing blood deficiency; localized blood stasis

Treatment:
Treatment was directed at restoring the strength of the Spleen qi in order to augment the blood, and moving blood stasis locally around the lesions. Selecting A# (the chromatic-scale tone for the Spleen meridian) as the primary fork, I supplemented Sp 10 while simultaneously supplementing Sp 11 with D# (the lower fifth of A#). I then repeated this same procedure with A# on Sp 6 and D# on Sp 7. Moxa was then applied to GV 14 to warm the yang channels.

I next drained the skin lesions on the lower extremities, using a C# fork in a circular motion to surround the lesions without touching them. I chose C# because of its ruler-ship over capillaries, which seemed to be the site of the stagnant blood in her skin.

The skin lesions were completely healed in two weeks, and had not returned after a follow-up call was made two months later.

Case History 5: Carpal Tunnel Syndrome

Practitioner: Dean Lloyd
Diagnostic Paradigm: Five-phase
Acutone Treatment Methodology: Five-phase Acutone using the pentatonic scale in both root and local treatment

A 34 year-old male, 5' 7", 128 lbs., complains of sharp pain in the medial aspect of the wrist due to carpal tunnel syndrome. At the first treatment, the pain score in the region of P 7 was "8" (1-10). In addition, there was a dull ache at the LI 10 region bilaterally. The patient worked at a computer in excess of 6 hours per day. He had been diagnosed with AIDS 5 years ago and was taking protease inhibitors. The patient had no other complaints besides the wrist pain.

Pulse: kidney position deficient
Diagnosis: Kidney Deficiency

Treatment:
I began by supplementing Ki 7 with D#, the pentatonic tone for Water, as the primary fork together with G#, the pentatonic tone for Metal, as the secondary fork. Next I supplemented Lu 8 with G# alone. This completed the root treatment.

For the local treatment I supplemented TW 4, Lu 9, Pc 7, and SI 4, all with D#. I then followed up with about 5 minutes of massage on both arms.

After finishing the session the patient's pain score had been reduced almost to zero. On previous occasions I had performed massage therapy, but had never experienced this dramatic an improvement.

Case History 6: Food Poisoning

Practitioner: Dean Lloyd
Diagnostic Paradigm: Modern Chinese
Acutone Treatment Methodology: Twelve-meridian Acutone using the chromatic scale in root and pentatonic scale in local treatment

A 44-year old male complained of nausea, belching, and abdominal pain following the consumption of stale food from his refrigerator earlier that day.

Pulse: slippery and deep
Tongue: thick and greasy
Diagnosis: Food Stagnation

Treatment:
Because of the patient's acute discomfort, I decided to do the local treatment first. I began by draining CV 12 and CV 13 with F#, the Earth tone. Then I focused on the Stomach meridian, selecting A (the tone ruling the Stomach meridian) as the primary fork and C# (the upper major third of A) as the secondary fork. Using these two forks simultaneously on each point, I drained St 21, St 25, St 34, St 36, and ST 37.

After the session, the patient stated that the nausea and abdominal pain had decreased about 50%, although he later reported that a sense of fullness remained until the next day.

Case History 7: Peripheral Neuropathy

Practitioner: John Pirog
Diagnostic Paradigm: Five-phase
Acutone Treatment Method: Local treatment using the pentatonic scale and heated crystals, used as an adjunct to acupuncture.

An 80 year-old man, 5' 8", 220 lbs., suffered from constant severe pain, tingling, and numbness in the palms and fingers of both hands, particularly in the middle, ring, and little fingers. The neuropathy had also affected the lower extremities, causing aching and numbness in the soles of both feet. In addition, he had had knee replacement surgery several years earlier. Because of all these factors, together with his obesity, he was able to walk only walk a few steps without support, requiring a wheel chair and an assistant to get around. About 6 months prior, this man had had coronary by-pass surgery, complications of which left him in a coma for over a month. The pain in his hands and feet began after awakening from the coma, and persisted even after leaving the hospital and normal cardiac function had been restored. Numerous tests had failed to firmly establish the cause of his pain, although it was assumed by his physicians that a peripheral neuropathy had developed as a result of the long period of immobilization. When he first came to visit me, he told me that the pain in his fingers was constant and severe.

Pulse: lung and kidney positions deficient
Diagnosis: Kidney Deficiency

Treatment:
I began the treatment with five-phase acupuncture, using contact stimulation with silver needles on Ki 7 and Lu 5, employing supplementation technique. I followed up with in-situ insertions and direct moxa on several *koris* I found in the region of Pc 3 and Pc 4 on both sides. I completed the treatment with a light pecking technique on the palms and on the Jing-Well points of the affected fingers.

After two months of intensive therapy (three visits weekly), the pain in the patient's hands and fingers gradually receded, becoming mild and intermittent, although it never disappeared completely. His general demeanor improved as well, and he began telling jokes with each visit.

I continued to see the patient for weekly maintenance treatments for over a year. Because the circulation in the lower extremities was compromised and there was a risk of infection, I had initially decided against using invasive needling in the lower extremities. But because the non-invasive root treatment alone was proving to be insufficient in bringing about any improvement in the pain and numbness in the patient's feet, I decided to supplement the acupuncture with a local Acutone treatment using heated quartz crystals.

I experimented with several different crystals from my collection and eventually found two that worked best (one for the left foot and one for the right). The crystals were stored in salt between treatments and were set aside for use on this patient only. The tuning fork I selected was D#, the Water tone, since I believed the problem originated in the deepest level of the tissue (see Chapter 2). I felt that D# was further indicated by the site of the points I had selected, all located on the soles of the feet, near the origin of the Kidney meridian at Ki 1.

Using the heated crystal technique described earlier in this chapter, I stimulated 4 or 5 points on each foot, locating the points by touch receptivity (tingling in my own fingers similar to the patient's description of his pain).

The treatments immediately brought relief. The pain in the patient's soles gradually became milder and more intermittent, just like the earlier treatments on the hands. The numbness, unfortunately, has not gone away, and the patient's ability to move around without assistance has only slightly improved. Furthermore, ongoing maintenance therapy has been necessary in order to prevent relapsing. But in spite of my failure to bring about a definitive "cure," the patient has expressed gratitude for the relief of pain and the improvement that the treatments have brought about in the quality of his life.

Case History 8

Practitioner: Dean Lloyd
Diagnostic paradigm: Five-phase
Acutone Treatment Method: Five-phase root and local treatment.

Treatment:
A 22 year old woman, 5' 6" 140 lbs., complained of migraine headaches. The headaches began 2 years prior when she was attending college. She described the pain as a dull, band-like sensation around the head which developed into sharp and almost paralyzing pain lasting anywhere from 20 minutes to several hours. At times the headaches would occur less than

once a month, at other times they would come two or three times a week. She was experiencing a relatively mild headache when she first came to see me, with a pain level of "3" (1-10).

Pulse: liver deficient, gall bladder excess

I began by resonating the treatment room with the frequency F#, the tone of the late summer. Because the patient was in pain when she came into the office, and the immediate presentation was one of excess, I chose to supplement the Liver meridian indirectly, by draining the Gall Bladder meridian. To do this I performed draining technique on GB 41, the Wood point and the same-phase point of the Gall Bladder meridian, using A# as the primary fork. I chose A# because it is the tone for Wood. The secondary fork was C#, the tone for Fire, the child of Wood. I used both of these forks simultaneously to drain GB 41. I then drained Tai Yang with A# alone.

The patient did not show any changer in her pain level during or immediately after the treatment. I subsequently performed some Shiatsu and this brought the pain down only slightly, to a "2" (1-10). The patient returned two weeks later. Although she had not experienced a severe migraine episode since the previous treatment, she once again was feeling moderate headache pain. The above treatment was repeated and once again there was no noticeable change.

Case History 9

Practitioner: Dean Lloyd
Diagnostic paradigm: Modern Chinese
Acutone Treatment Method: Twelve-meridian Acutone with local treatment using the pentatonic scale

A 15-year old male came to my office for treatment of acute neck pain together with a headache. He rated the neck pain at a level of "7" (1-10). He said that he had caught a cold when surfing with friends a few days ago; and while other symptoms had run their course, the headache still remained. The right side was significantly more painful than the left, and he complained that several times a day his neck would "pop" when he moved it.

Tongue: red with raised red papillae, yellow coat
Pulse: rapid floating
Diagnosis: Wind-Heat

Treatment:
I began by draining the Shu-back point for the Lung, UB 13, using G#, the pentatonic tone for the Lung. I next drained the Lung channel on the left (asymptomatic) side using G (the tone on the chromatic scale for the Lung meridian) on Lu 10 and B (the upper major third of G) on Lu 7. I then drained LI 4, again on the left side, using G# (the chromatic-scale tone for the Large Intestine meridian) as the primary fork and C (the upper major third of G#) as the secondary tone.

Finally, I turned my attention to several *Ashi* points on the right (symptomatic) side of the neck, dispersing each for one or two seconds with G# alone. The G# fork was chosen for local treatment because I judged the primary pathogen to be external wind.

The patient's pain score soon dropped to a "3" (1-10) and the patient reported feeling more invigorated and simultaneously more relaxed. The pulse was checked after the treatment; it had slowed down and the floating quality had disappeared.

Appendix A

The Search for the Missing Huang Zhong

The authors discovered early in their research that the fundamental frequency of the Chinese scale—the tone of the *Huang Zhong-Gong* pitch-pipe—was of vital importance to the effectiveness of Acutone treatment. This frequency was not arbitrarily chosen by the Chinese musical sages; it represented a mystical heritage that they took great pains to discover and preserve from one generation to the next[41]. It was this frequency that the authors of the *Ling Shu (Mystical Pivot)* had in mind when they assigned the notes of the pentatonic scale to the five-phases and their associated organs and meridians[42]. Any attempt to make a therapeutic application of sound using acupuncture meridians must therefore be based on the authentic *Huang Zhong* frequency of the late Zhou and early Han dynasties.

---

[41] Von Falkenhausen, p. 317.

[42] *Ling Shu (Mystical Pivot*, Liansheng Wu, Nelson and Andrew Qi Wu, transl.) ch. 64, 65.

In Chapter 5 we demonstrated the striking symmetry between the lower frequencies of audible sound and the higher frequencies contained in the "octave" of visible light. We explained how the higher-octave F, being the approximate beginning and ending point of the visible spectrum, could logically be seen as the key note of the scale of sound as well. We further explained how this note must ultimately be derived from the *Gong* pitch of the pentatonic scale, F# (see also Appendix B). Based on this mystical correspondence between light and sound, seeing and hearing, we believe that the modern note F# is the closest representative of the Han dynasty *Huang Zhong-Gong*.

But what evidence do we have that F# is the frequency that the ancient Chinese actually used? An intact pitch-pipe from the Han or Zhou dynasty has not survived, and any attempt to calculate frequencies based on descriptions in the Classics is hampered by the fact that these sources recorded only pitch-pipe lengths, not diameters. Furthermore, any measurement of frequency will vary slightly depending on air temperature and humidity. Thus, a pitch-pipe blown in the morning, when the humidity is high and the air is cold, would be slightly sharper than the same pipe blown in the evening.

Yet in spite of these uncertainties, there has long been a consensus among musical archaeologists that the Han Dynasty *Huang Zhong* fundamental must have fallen somewhere between the modern F and G#. This assumption has been based on the *Huang Zhong* length of 1 *chi* (i.e. 10 *cun*) recorded in the *Lu Shi Chun Qiu* (*Springs and Autumns of Master Lu*, c. 235 B.C.). The length of a Han Dynasty *chi* is believed to be 230.89 mm or 9.09 English inches[43].

In 1860, the French researcher Chavannes estimated the frequency of the *Huang Zhong* pipe at 15 °C to be 777.7 Hz[44], assuming a length of 1 *chi* and a diameter of 0.3 *cun*. Using this

---

[43] Liu Fu, 1934, p. 999, Chen Qiyou 1962, p. 186; compare with Huang Xiang-Peng, p. 272-280.
[44] Liu Fu, 1934, p. 999.

same length but a larger diameter of .7272 *chi*, this frequency was later corrected to 723.9 Hz by Liu Fu[45] in 1934, making the *Huang Zhong* pitch slightly flatter than the F#$_5$ (739.99 Hz) of a modern tempered A440 scale (see Table A.1). In 1962 Chen Qiyou recalculated the frequency with a slightly different formula, assuming a 9 *cun* length and 0.3 *cun* diameter. He obtained a frequency of 388.8 Hz, i.e., about an octave lower than the earlier Chavannes estimate, and slightly flatter than the modern G$_4$ (392 Hz).[46]

Source	Frequency (Hz)
F$_4$	349.23
Marquis Yi Set-Bell T-2-6, *Gong* mode (extrapolated)	364.50
F#$_4$	369.99
Chen Qiyou, 1962	388.80
G$_4$	392.00
Marquis Yi Set-Bell T-2-6, *Shang* mode	410.10
G#$_4$	415.30
F$_5$	698.46
Liu Fu, 1934	723.90
F#$_5$	739.99
Chavannes, 1860	777.70
G$_5$	783.99

Table A.1 Comparison of Various Huang Zhong Frequency Estimates With Modern Pitch standards of A 440 Scale

But while all these values are speculative, a concrete reconstruction of the *Huang Zhong* frequency of the Zhou dynasty can now be accomplished thanks to the 1978 discovery of 65 set-bells in the tomb of the Marquis Yi. Excavated in the modern province of Hubei, China, the tomb dates to the 5th century B.C., placing it in the early Warring States period. By far the

---

[45] Liu Fu, 1934, p. 999.
[46] Chen Qiyou, 1962, p. 186.

most well preserved instruments from Chinese antiquity, the Marquis Yi set-bells provide us with explicit, acoustically verifiable information on the frequencies of a number of standard pitches from the Zhou dynasty. The various strike zones of these bells are labeled with pitches drawn from the twelve notes of the chromatic scale, in many cases coupled with notes indicating specific modes of the pentatonic scale.

The inscriptions on the central strike zone of bell T-2-6 indicate that this tone represents the *Huang Zhong* pitch in the *Shang* mode. Acoustic readings taken in 1979[47] measure the frequency of this bell at 410.1 Hz[48]. This is slightly flatter than the modern G#$_4$ (415.3 Hz), the authors' assumed value for the pentatonic *Shang* note (see Chapter 2).

As we demonstrated in Chapter 2, it is the *Gong* mode that aligns the pentatonic scale most perfectly with the five-phase cosmological patterns utilized in Chinese medicine. Although no other bells are inscribed with the *Huang Zhong* characters, we can extrapolate the frequency of the *Huang Zhong* pitch in the *Gong* mode from bell T-2-6 by moving its fundamental down by a major second, or 8/9. Thus:

8/9 X 410.1 = 364.5

This gives us a theoretical *Huang Zhong* frequency from the 5th century B.C. of 364.5 Hz, tantalizingly close to the modern F#$_4$ frequency of 369.99 Hz.

Although we feel confident that F# is the most accurate fundamental for Acutone purposes, we cannot rule out the potential effectiveness of a Chinese scale based on G or even G#, these tones falling within the limits inherent in the various *Huang Zhong* estimates quoted above. But we must warn the reader that, although some flexibility in setting pitch standards in Acutone might be permissible, we must not let ourselves wan-

---

[47] Feng Guang-Sheng and Tan Wei-Si, 1988.
[48] Chen Cheng-Yih, 1996, p. 46.

der too far afield. Our goal as Oriental medical practitioners is to recapture the lost wisdom of the past, and to make sure that the current application fits the system for which it was designed. Our experience has shown that changing the traditional *Huang Zhong* by more than a major second can produce results that are contrary to the intentions of the practitioner.

The ancient musical sages considered the *Huang Zhong* fundamental a sacred relic passed down from their ancestors, and took great pains to preserve its accuracy. Pitch standards in all cultures are easily lost, driven ever higher by the desires of soprano singers to upstage their bass and baritone counterparts, and by the demands of brass military bands for more intense marching music[49]. Eventually, even the Chinese lost touch with their musical roots, as the founders of each new dynasty sought to impose their authority by making small adjustments in the *Huang Zhong*, with at least 31 changes having been recorded down to 1911[50]. Worse of all, the most recent changes have been made to accommodate Western music, and so predictably, the modern standard for *Gong-Huang Zhong* has been raised to C[51]. As we have learned throughout this book, it is music that defines the civilization, and the acceptance of Western pitch standards represents a most deep and insidious loss of traditional Chinese cultural wisdom.

This brings us to one final issue. As we learned in Chapter 2, the frequencies of modern chromatic tuning forks are set in a *Tempered* scale, while the Zhou dynasty theory of generating pitches produced a *Just* scale. In a tempered scale, the intervals are mathematically "evened out" to allow change of key with the minimum number of notes. As a result, the frequencies of

---

[49] Wood, p. 46-49.

[50] Von Falkenhausen, p. 317-318.

[51] The reader must be cautioned to read modern Sinological works carefully in regard to this issue. In many cases, the ancient *Huang Zhong* is represented as C in order to allow easier analysis of musical intervals. See for example Fung Yu-lan, 1934, p. 11 and Chen Cheng-Yih, Xi Ze-Zong, and Jao Tsung-I, 1994, p. 320.

the notes change slightly and the fifths and octaves are slightly out of tune.

In our early work with Acutone, we learned that these differences were too small to affect treatment outcome. In fact, acoustical readings made on the Marquis Yi set bells proves that the Chinese themselves were tempering their scales as early as the Zhou dynasty[52]. Although these early attempts were the result of crude arithmetic progression, a more elegant system was designed by Zhu Zaiyu in 1584, based on the geometric relationship between the circumscribed square and circle of Chinese cosmology[53]. This suggests that tempering has been an intrinsic element of traditional Chinese instrument construction. We can conclude, therefore, that so long as we are using the correct fundamental, the use of our tempered tuning forks will not violate the spirit of the ancient Chinese scale system.

[52] Von Falkenhausen, p. 92-96.
[53] Chen Chen-Yih, 1999.

Appendix B

The Chinese Chromatic Scale In Detail

As we learned in Chapter 5, the Chinese musical sages believed that each frequency had a life of its own, and that each pitch in the scale had a natural "desire" to generate the fifth above it. We explained that there is no upper fifth in the pentatonic scale for *Jue* (A#), and so it must generate a new note outside the range of the pentatonic gamut of tones. This new note, as we have learned, is *Huang Zhong* (F-natural), which gives birth to a whole new scale of twelve notes, each linked with its upper fifth in a perfect self-enclosed circle (refer back to Figure 5.2).

If the chromatic scale is truly being generated from the pentatonic scale—or vice versa— there would need to be a half-step difference between *Gong* (F#) and *Huang Zhong* (F-natural). At first glance this would appear to contradict the *Shi Ji* (*Record of the Historian*, c. 2nd century B.C.), which seems to establish the frequency of both notes on the 8.1-*cun* pitch pipe.[54] Although the link we have described between the gene-sis of the two scales is symbolically valid, is there any evidence that it played a real role in scale construction?

While information on this subject is somewhat speculative, there is some evidence to suggest that, before the standardiza-tion of pitches that took place in the early Han Dynasty, the fun-damental of the chromatic scale—the *Huang Zhong* pitch—was itself generated from a mysterious unnamed note.[55]

Prior to the Han Dynasty, the five tones of the pentatonic scale did not necessarily have fixed frequencies. The terms *Gong-Shang-Jue-Zhi-Yu* were used as a kind of solmization system, functioning in Zhou Dynasty music in much the same way that the terms *do-re-mi* etc. are used today.[56] Their purpose in music was to establish *intervals*, not absolute frequency. Table B.1 displays the modern sol-fa equivalents for the five tones:

Gong	Shang	Jue	Zhi	Yu
Do	Re	Mi	Sol	La

Table B.1 Sol-Fa Equivalents of the Five Pentatonic Notes

---

[54] As translated in Von Falkenhausen, p. 300.

[55] The relevant passage is in the *Lu Shi Chun Qiu* (*Springs and Autumns of Master Lu*, c. 3rd century B.C.), as quoted and described by Chen Cheng Yi (1994 pp. 170, 180).

[56] Von Falkenhausen, p. 282.

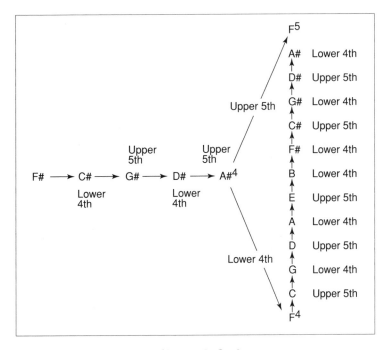

Figure B.1 Generating the Chromatic Scale

It was the role of the twelve pitch-pipes to establish the standards of frequency, and thus the "Do" (*Gong*) could be set at any pitch-key in this larger scale. Music played on the pentatonic scale, therefore, could be transposed to twelve different keys, and this was referred to as the "sliding *Gong*" (*xuan Gong*) principle. We must therefore conclude that the identification of the *Gong* pitch with the *Huang Zhong* pitch-pipe described in the *Shi Ji* above was meant only as a key-note of common musical reference, in much the same way that the key of C is typically referred to when describing a modern major scale.

We have taken pains to explain that *one* specific frequency was considered by the ancient Chinese to be the all-important link with their ancestors, and that this frequency, usually referred to as *Huang Zhong*, was the cornerstone of all scales. A special problem presented itself, however, when the *Huang Zhong* was used by itself to create a chromatic scale. As we learned in

Chapter 1, all true scales must have be based on an octave. During the Zhou Dynasty the Chinese learned, just as the Greeks were learning at roughly the same time in the West, that a twelve-note scale generated entirely out of fifths does not produce a perfect octave.

Let us continue to assume that the *Huang Zhong* pitch-pipe had a frequency akin to F_4. If we successively increase and decrease the *Huang Zhong* length by 1/3, just as we did when we built the pentatonic scale in Chapter 1, we will produce all the notes of the chromatic scale (Figure B.1). If our scale is to be perfect, however, the twelfth pitch-pipe thus generated—F_5—will need to be *exactly double* the length of the original F_4-pipe. But if we use the method of increasing and decreasing just described, the final F_5-pipe will be *slightly more* than double the length of the original F_4. This mathematical "error," referred to as a *Pythagorean comma* in Western musicology, was corrected by the Chinese sages with a unique solution.

A perfect octave can be generated from a single pitch pipe using the 1/3 increase-decrease method described above. To demonstrate this, let us start with a single pitch pipe X (Figure B.2) and use its length as a reference for generating two additional pipes. We will make the second pipe Y_1 4/3 the length of X, and the third pipe Y_2 we will make 2/3 the length of X. The pitch of Y_1 will be a lower fourth of X, and that of Y_2 will be an upper fifth of X. Y_1 will be double the length of Y_2, and therefore the *two pipes will be exactly one octave apart*.

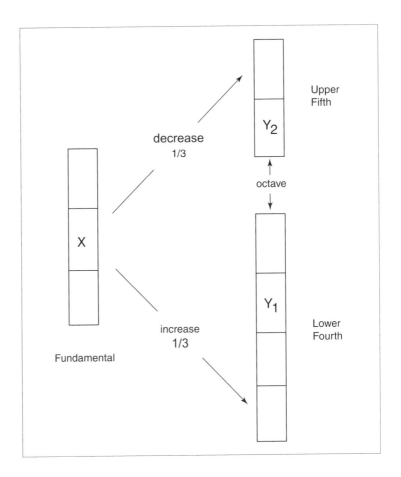

Figure B.2 Generating an Octave From a Single Pitch-Pipe

In Figure B.1, we show how the *Jue* (A#) pitch pipe could have been used in exactly this manner to supply the perfect octave between the two *Huang Zhong's*, F_4 and F_5. Assuming the frequency of *Jue* to be equivalent to $A\#_4$, a 1/3 decrease in its length would have generated F_5, its upper fifth, and a 1/3 increase in $A\#_4$ would have generated F_4, its lower fourth. If we then took A# and continued to worked our way back through the generation of fifths we would have reproduced all the notes of the pentatonic scale at the same frequencies described in Chapter 1, ending with *Gong at F#*.

In short, the *Huang Zhong* cannot be used to make a complete scale all by itself. The pentatonic scale, therefore, was more than just a theoretical precursor to the chromatic scale, it was a practical necessity in the process of generating the perfect octave. While the frequency of *Gong* could be allowed to "slide" once the twelve-pitch scale was actually completed, the original creation of such a scale necessitated a pre-existing *Gong* of a fixed frequency defined as 1/2 step distant from the chromatic fundamental. This "precursor *Gong*" would then generate the successive pitches of the pentatonic scale ending with *Jue*, which would then generate the higher and lower octaves of the *Huang Zhong* pitch-pipes.

To be sure, the A# needed to create the higher-octave F could have been generated using the increase-decrease method from F itself; alternatively the F pitch-pipe could have been simply cut in half to create a higher octave. The Acutone techniques presented in this book, however, are making use of the scale to control the energetic creation process itself, and this necessitates that we return to the first ultimate principles of scale creation. By assuming a universal *Gong* frequency of F# and separate it from the fundamental of the chromatic scale by a half-step, we can best exploit the intergenerational relationship between the pitches of these two great scales. In this manner, the notes of the pentatonic scale will always blend harmoniously with the frequencies of the meridian upon which they are used.

Appendix
C

Time Adjustments For Acutone

The human body and its circulating energy is synchronized with the transit of the *true sun*, i.e., the actual sun as it appears in the heavens. The twelve-hour Chinese "clock" is therefore a kind of sundial (see Chapter 5, Figure 5.1). The true astronomical sun does *not* form the basis of modern civil time, however. Instead, modern clocks are set to a mean "imaginary" sun that—unlike the true sun—transits through the heavens at a fixed rate. To make matters worse, clocks around the world are adjusted to standard time meridians that might be hundreds of miles from their actual geographic location. Finally, there is Daylight Savings Time, which creates a massive one-hour discrepancy with the true sundial time.

Thus, the clock hanging on your wall is not the clock your meridian circulation is responding to, and it is not the clock you need to follow if you are using the twelve-hour meridian wheel in therapy. We recommend keeping a separate "sundial clock" in your office, upon which the following adjustments have been made.

Step 1. Adjust for Daylight Savings Time.

If daylight savings time is in effect, subtract one hour.

Step 2. Adjust for distance from Standard Time Meridian.

If your office is located East of the standard meridian for your time zone, add 4 minutes of clock time for each degree longitude you are East of the meridian. If you are West of the meridian, subtract 4 minutes for each degree you are West of the meridian. The longitude of your office can be determined from a map.

Example: Office location: Chicago. Clocks are set to the Central Standard Meridian, which is 90° West longitude. Chicago itself is 88° West longitude, 2° East of the Central Standard Meridian. We must add 4 minutes for each degree East of the meridian: 2 x 4 minutes = 8 minutes. So we add 8 minutes to the clock.

Step 3. Add the equation of time (E/T)

The equation of time is the difference in minutes between the true sun and the mean imaginary sun. This value is positive when the true sun is West of the mean sun, and negative when East of the mean sun. The value of E/T can be calculated or copied directly from a Nautical Ephemeris. Since the value of E/T varies continuously throughout the year, frequent corrections will be needed to keep the sundial clock accurate. The limiting and zero values of E/T are listed on Table C.1 below.

Month	Minutes
December	0.00
February	−14.25
April	0.00
May	+03.75
June	0.00
July	−06.50
September	0.00
November	+16.25

Table C.1 Equation of Time (E/T)

Appendix
D

How to Purchase Equipment

In order to apply the techniques explained in this book, the reader will need to obtain a full **Chromatic octave** of stainless steel or nickel tuning forks. Recall that chromatic scales include all the half-tones, so a full set will contain a total of thirteen forks labeled from C_4 to C_5. As of this writing, there are only two companies world-wide that make high-quality chromatic tuning fork sets. The tuning fork sets commonly available in music stores and through New Age suppliers contain only a *diatonic octave* (eight forks with no half-tones), which is not adequate for Acutone work.

The reader can obtain chromatic tuning forks, Resonator Bells (see Figure 2.13A), and other Acutone equipment by contacting us at our web site:

www.acutone.com

or by writing to:

La Mesa Holistic Health Center
8356 Allison Avenue #B2
LaMesa, California 91941

Bibliography

Chen Qi-You, 1962, "Huang Zhong Guan Chang-Kao," *Zhonghua Wenshi Luncong* I: 183-188.

Chen Cheng-Yih, edit., 1994, *Two-Tone Set-Bells of Marquis Yi*, World Scientific Publishing Co., Singapore.

Chen Cheng Yih, Xi Ze-Zong, Jao Tsung-I, 1994 "A Comparative Study of Acoustics and Astronomy in Babylonia and in China Prior to and During the Time of Marquis Yi Set-Bells," Chen Cheng-Yih, edit., *Two-Tone Set-Bells of Marquis Yi*, World Scientific Publishing Co., Singapore.

Chen Cheng-Yih 1996, *Early Chinese Work in Natural Science: A Re-examination of the Physics of Motion, Acoustics, Astronomy and Scientific Thoughts*, Hong Kong University Press.

Chen Cheng-Yih, 1999, "Re-visit of the Work of Zhu Zaiyu in Acoustics," *Current Perspectives in the History of Science in East Asia*, Seol University Press.

Cheng Xinnong, 1987, *Chinese Acupuncture and Moxabustion*, Foreign Languages Press, Beijing.

Ellis, Andrew, Nigel Wiseman, and Ken Boss, 1988, *Fundamentals of Chinese Acupuncture*, Paradigm Publications, Brookline, Massachusetts.

Ellis, Andrew, Nigel Wiseman, and Ken Boss, 1989, *Grasping the Wind*, Paradigm Publications, Brookline, Massachusetts.

Elson, Louis C., 1909, *Elson's Pocket Music Dictionary*, Oliver Ditson Co., Bryn Mawr, Pennsylvania.

Feng Guang-Sheng and Tan Wei-Si, 1994 "Discovery and Research of the Marquis Yi Set-Bells," Chen Cheng-Yih, edit., *Two-Tone Set-Bells of Marquis Yi*, World Scientific Publishing Co., Singapore.

Fung Yu-Lan, 1931, *A History of Chinese Pholosophy: Vol. I: The Period of the Philosophers*, trans. Derk Bodde, 2nd ed. in English, 1953, Princeton University Press, Princeton.

Fung Yu-Lan, 1934, *A History of Chinese Philosophy: Vol. II: The Period of Classical Learning*, trans. Derk Bodde, 1953, Princeton University Press, Princeton.

Goetschius, Percy, 1931, *The Theory and Practice of Tone-Relations: an Elementary Course of Harmony with Emphasis Upon the Element of Melody*, 24th ed., G. Schirmer Inc., New York.

Huang Xiang-Peng, 1994 "A Study of the Jun-Zhong, a Five-String Instrument," Chen Cheng-Yih, edit., *Two-Tone Set-Bells of Marquis Yi*, World Scientific Publishing Co., Singapore.

Levis, John Hazedel, 1936, *Foundation of Chinese Musical Art*, 1st ed. Peking, reprint 1963 Paragon Books, New York.

Liansheng Wu, Nelson and Andrew Qi Wu, transl., 1999, *Yellow Emperor's Canon of Internal Medicine (Huang Di Nei Jing)*, China Science and Technology Press, Beijing.

Liu Fu, 1934, *"Lu Shi Chun Qiu* 'Gu Yue-Pian' Huang Zhong Jie Jie," *Wen Xue* (Shanghai), 2 (6): 993-1001.

Maman, Fabien, 1997a, *Book I, The Role of Music in the Twenty-first Century*, Tama-Do Press, P.O. Box 7000-746, Redondo Beach, California, 90277.

Maman, Fabien, 1997b, *Book II, Raising Human Frequencies: The Way of Chi and the Subtle Bodies*, Tama-Do Press, P.O. Box 7000-746, Redondo Beach, California, 90277.

Maman, Fabien, 1997c, *Book III, The Body As Harp: Sound and Acupuncture*, Tama-Do Press, P.O. Box 7000-746, Redondo Beach, California, 90277.

Maman, Fabien, 1997d, *Book IV, Healing With Sound, Color and Movement: Nine Evolutionary Healing Techniques*, Tama-Do Press, P.O. Box 7000-746, Redondo Beach, California, 90277.

Needham, Joseph, 1956, *Science and Civilization in China, Vol. II: The History of Scientific Thought*, Cambridge University Press, Cambridge.

Pirog, John E., 1996, *Practical Application of Meridian-Style Acupuncture*, Pacific View Press, Berkley, California.

Price, Lew Paxton, 1995, *The Oldest Magic: the pre history, ancient history, nature of, and early influence of Music with special attention to the role of the Flute*, Lew Paxton Price, P.O. Box 88, Garden Valley, California, 95633.

Taylor, Charles, 1992, *Exploring Music: the Science and Technology of Tones and Tunes*, Institute of Physics Publishing, Bristol and Philadelphia.

Von Falkenhausen, Lothar, 1993, *Suspended Music: Chime-Bells in the Culture of Bronze Age China*, University of California Press, Berkley and Los Angeles, California.

Walters, Derek, 1987, *Chinese Astrology*, Borgo Press, San Fernando, California.

Wood, Alexander, 1975, rev. J. M. Bowsher, 7th ed., *The Physics of Music*, Greenwood Press, Westport, Connecticut.